OSS Special Weapons & Equipment

SPY DEVICES of WWII

H. Keith Melton

Foreword by William Colby,
former Director of
Central Intelligence

 Sterling Publishing Co., Inc.   New York

Acknowledgments

For their gracious assistance during the preparation of this volume: Mr. Arnold Ross; The Hon. William E. Colby; Hayden Peake; Elizabeth Bancroft; Tom Troy; Jeff Jones, Veterans of the OSS;
John Minnery; Major Johnny "B-2" Brown; Dr. John Brunner; I.D. Skennerton; Bill Henhoeffer and Linda McCarty, of the CIA's Historical Intelligence Collection;
Pierre Lorain; David Kahn; Gary Cain; Lloyd R. Shoemaker; Albert R. Materazzi; Cdr. George Graveson; James Ladd.

With appreciation for the use of the following photographs and material: Dr. John Brunner, pages 45 and 46; John Minnery, page 37; Major W.E. Fairbairn, pages 16 and 17; Ian Skennerton, pages 39 and 43; Wm. Cassidy, page 118; Louis F. Fieser, page 10; Kermit Roosevelt, War Report of the·OSS, pages 11 and 12; David Kahn, page 81; Vannevar Bush, page 8; Clayton Hutton, page 47.

Edited by Rodman P. van Oss

Special recognition for their knowledge and assistance in writing on historical intelligence equipment: Capt. Peter Mason, SAS, Ret., Canada's premier expert on clandestine weapons and devices; Dr. Walter L. Pforzheimer, the Dean of Intelligence Bibliophiles and curator of the extraordinary Pforzheimer Collection.

10 9 8 7 6 5 4 3 2 1

© 1991 by H. Keith Melton
Published by Sterling Publishing Company, Inc.
387 Park Avenue South, New York, N.Y. 10016
Distributed in Canada by Sterling Publishing
% Canadian Manda Group, P.O. Box 920, Station U
Toronto, Ontario, Canada M8Z 5P9
Distributed in Great Britain and Europe by Cassell PLC
Villiers House, 41/47 Strand, London WC2N 5JE, England
Distributed in Australia by Capricorn Ltd.
P.O. Box 665, Lane Cove, NSW 2066
Manufactured in the United States of America
All rights reserved

Sterling ISBN 0-8069-8238-1

Library of Congress Cataloging-in-Publication Data

Melton, H. Keith (Harold Keith), 1944–
    OSS special weapons & equipment : spy devices of W.W. II / by H. Keith Melton ; foreword by William E. Colby.
        p.   cm.
    Includes bibliographical references and index.
    ISBN 0-8069-8238-1
    1. Military intelligence—United States—Equipment and supplies—Handbooks, manuals, etc.   2. Sabotage—United States—Equipment and supplies—Handbooks, manuals, etc.   3. Espionage—United States—Equipment and supplies—Handbooks, manuals, etc.   I. Title.
II. Title: OSS special weapons and equipment.
UB271.U5M44   1991
355.3'432'028—dc20   90-22118
                                                                          CIP

Contents

Foreword by William Colby, former Director of Central Intelligence   5

Introduction   7

History of the National Defense Research Committee   8

Office of Strategic Services Research and Development Branch History   11

Original OSS Weapons Manual, June 1944 Cover   13

Personal Weapons   15

Fighting Knife   15
Small Fighting Knife   16
Sleeve Dagger   18
Lapel Knife   19
Frisk Knife   20
Gravity Knife   21
Smatchet   22
Spring Cosh   24
Garrote   26
Peskett Close Combat Weapon   27
Knuckles   28
Stinger   29
En-Pen   30
.22 Caliber Cigarette   31
Pipe Pistol   32
Cigar Pistol   33
Liberator (Woolworth Gun)   34
Silenced .22 Caliber Automatic
    Pistol   36
Welrod   37
Glove Pistol   38
Belt-Gun   39
.32 Caliber Colt Pistol   40
Silenced Barrel for M3 .45 Cal.
    Sub-Machine Gun   41
Sniper's Rifle With Silencer   42
DeLisle Carbine   43
Bigot   44
Little Joe   45
William Tell   46
Dart-Pen   47
Air-Pen   48

Incendiaries   49

Pocket Incendiary M1   49
Large Thermit Well   51
Small Thermit Well   53
City Slicker (Oil Slick Igniter)   55
Incendiary Packet   56
Capsules H   57

Explosives   58

Limpet   58
Pin-Up Girl (Limpet With Pinning
    Device)   60
Clam   62
Fog Signal   64
Mole   65
Anerometer   67
Beano   69
Explosive Coal   70
Coal Camouflage Kit   71

Communications Equipment   72

SSTR-1 Suitcase Radio   72
SSR-5 Miniature Radio   73
AN/PRC-1 Suitcase Radio   74
AN/PRC-5 Suitcase Radio   75
SCR-504 Direction Finding
    Radio   76
Type B, Mark II Suitcase Radio   77
Type A, Mark III Suitcase Radio   78
M-209 Cipher Machine   79
M-94 Cipher Device   81
One-Time Pad   82

Harassing Agents 83

Who, Me? 83
Dog Drag 84

Automotive Attack 85

Firefly (Incendiary Explosive) 85
Caccolube 86
Tire Spike 88
Saboteur's Knife 89

Firing Devices 90

Firing Device—Pressure Type
A-3 90
Firing Device—Release Type
A-2 92
Firing Device—Pull Type A-2 94
Time Delay Pencils 95
AC Delay 97
MK.3 (Clock) 99

Accessories 100

Adhesive Paste 100
Adhesive Tape 100
Plastic Explosive (P.E.) and
Primacord 101
Detonator Magazine 102

Magnets 102
Match Box (Camera) 103
Minox Miniature Camera 105
Gilhooley 107
Press X 108
Medical Kit 109
Lockpick Knife 110
Escape Knife 111
Escape Kit 112
Button Compass 113
Sleeping Beauty 114
Welbike 116
Jump Suit 117

Appendix 118

OSS Supplies at Algiers Base, Spring
1943 118
Identification Cards, Insignia, Farewell
Letter, and Certificate 119

Glossary 123

OSS Research Projects, Special
Devices, and Terminology 123

Bibliography 127

Index 128

Foreword

The Office of Strategic Services (OSS) was an exercise in improvisation. When the United States entered World War II, President Franklin Roosevelt turned to an old friend from New York, William J. Donovan, and asked him to establish an intelligence service to help the country fight the war. Donovan accepted the challenge with enthusiasm, even though he was aware that the nation had to build one from the ground up.

Roosevelt chose the right man. A certified World War I hero with the Medal of Honor, Donovan displayed courage that was matched by his intellectual curiosity and combative lawyer's mind, as well as his willingness to seek new solutions to old or new problems and to try any way of achieving his nation's objectives. He looked to the British to benefit from their two hundred years of intelligence work, to the scientific and technological communities for the special tools the new information gathering tasks would require, and to our nation's universities for the analysts and researchers who could turn information into intelligence.

Donovan united all of these elements to create the Office of Strategic Services, and told them to get on with the main job of fighting the nation's enemies at the same time they were learning how to do it. He was open to every idea; some turned out well, some badly, but he kept the pressure on in any case. Faced with brutal and deadly enemies, the OSS went to work as hard as it could, and the polite arts of peacetime yielded to the rough requirements of total war.

H. Keith Melton is one of the greatest of students and collectors of that grim but finally triumphant period of our history. He has assembled a brilliant collection of the devices developed and used in that struggle for freedom. This book presents the collection by reproducing the very descriptions of the weapons and devices which the OSS itself used to explain their use and workings to the many heroes, of the United States and Allies, who turned them so effectively against our then common enemies in Europe and Asia.

To many of us the collection brings a smile of recognition as we see the Fighting Knife that we carried and trained to use, the Time Delay Pencils and firing devices that we used for booby traps, or the Limpets or Moles that we knew were supplied to some of the great resistance fighters with whom we worked. For others, the collection will show how we developed the tools of secret warfare, so that brave peoples could fight against a fierce occupier.

But perhaps most timely, the collection shows the kinds of weapons which the civilized world must learn to counter and defend itself against when fanatical terrorists turn to attacks on innocent citizens, air travellers, or mere bystanders to their struggles. This book gives away no secrets in these fields today, as today's terrorists regrettably have even more sophisticated devices at their disposal, but it does show the patriotic citizen the type of threat we all face. It should also give some measure of encouragement that if the United States was able to develop the tools for secret warfare under the OSS, it might be equally effective now in developing the necessary tools and devices for countering terrorists and other enemies of civilization.

William Colby
Member of OSS, 1943–1945
Director of Central Intelligence,
1973–1976

Four Norwegian-speaking Americans, who parachuted into Norway in March 1945 to assist the underground movement as members of the American "Task Force A." They are from left to right: Borge Langeland, Brooklyn, NY; Cpl. Kai Johnson, Brooklyn, NY, who was born at Arendal; Maj. William E. Colby, St. Paul, MN; and T/Sgt. Matti Raivio, Brooklyn, NY, who was born in Finland. Oslo, Norway, 16 June 1945

Maj. Colby would later become Director of Central Intelligence (DCI). Note also that he is wearing the "SF" wings on his right shoulder (refer to Appendix, page 119).

Introduction

During World War II, science and technology were applied to the development of new instruments of warfare that utilized many kinds of scientific principles. The results were remarkable, and warfare thereby assumed previously unthought of tactical aspects. For the first time in history, the outcome of a war was largely determined by emergent technology that did not exist at the onset of hostilities!

The combined efforts of Division 19 and the Research and Development Branch of the OSS resulted in no single discovery that ranks with radar or the atomic bomb. However, a number of novel and innovative devices (shown herein) were developed primarily for individuals or small groups of "special forces" personnel operating behind enemy lines. Considerable imagination was shown in the creation of these devices, and they required an equal imagination on the part of potential users. The highly unorthodox nature of the devices allowed a very narrow field of application. This is not to say, however, that the value of such unorthodox devices might not be of the highest degree for a given individual in a particular situation while operating behind enemy lines! For this reason, even such limited demand and narrow application justified the creation and production of special weapons, devices, and equipment that were virtually unknown at the beginning of the war.

To disseminate information to its scattered bases and personnel, in July of 1944 the OSS published a "Sears and Roebuck"-style catalog which described and pictured each piece of specialized equipment. This catalog of spy equipment gives historians a unique insight into the weapons and technical devices of the OSS. The original 1944 catalog, reproduced here, is exceedingly rare. Only a limited number were produced, and of these, only a handful exist today.

Using the 1944 catalog as a base, I have updated it to include weapons, devices, and equipment that were being designed and produced up to the very end of the war. Because of the commonality of design between the OSS and the SOE (British Special Operations, Executive) equipment, some examples of SOE equipment have been added *if they were available to OSS personnel either in their training, or in the field*. The presence of an asterisk following the item's name will indicate that this page has been added to update the original 1944 publication.

Some of the special pieces of equipment developed for the OSS began as innovative ideas that evolved into highly effective instruments of subversive warfare. A few of the weapons and devices have remained so useful that they can still be found in the arsenals of our intelligence agencies.

From deadly, bullet-firing cigarettes to cameras hidden in match boxes, the specialized equipment of the OSS was unique. These intriguing, innovative and sometimes deadly devices have had a lasting effect on the world of clandestine warfare and peacetime operations!

The author welcomes correspondence related to espionage devices, weapons, and equipment of any period.

—H. Keith Melton

History of the National Defense Research Committee

The idea that scientists and the military establish a partnership for the development of new weapons is not a new concept. Abraham Lincoln gave expression to this idea during the Civil War when he established the American Academy of Sciences. The Academy, and the subsequent National Defense Council of World War I, maintained an ongoing relationship between scientists and the military. Though these partnerships explored new ideas for weapons and war-related technology, their success was limited by inadequate funding and a lack of overall authority.

In the years preceding 1940 events revealed more and more clearly the seriousness of the world situation. Many scientists in the United States came to realize the need of organizing scientific research for service in the event of a national emergency. Their recommendations which were made to the White House were given careful and sympathetic attention. As a result, the National Defense Research Committee (NDRC) was formed by Executive Order of the President in the summer of 1940.

The members of the NDRC, appointed by the President of the United States of America, were instructed to supplement the work of the US Army and US Navy in *"the development of the instrumentalities of war."* A year later, upon establishment of the Office of Scientific Research and Development (OSRD), NDRC became one of its units. The NDRC and OSRD, together, researched and developed new weapons and devices, and met with the War and Navy Departments—as well as other agencies of the US Federal Government—to discuss their application in national defense.

As the war in Europe continued, the NDRC realized that the British had extensive knowledge of new German weaponry as well as experience in developing countermeasures. In February of 1941, President Roosevelt sent James B. Conant, cofounder of the NDRC, to England to make arrangements for an exchange of technical information, and to establish an NDRC office in London. This scientific relationship with the British was to flourish throughout the war. The British shared their research and experience with the NDRC. The NDRC, in exchange, facilitated the acquisition of needed technical equipment and electronic components for war-ravaged British industries. *So successful was this relationship, that by the end of the war, it was frequently not possible to distinguish between British and United States technology!*

In late 1942, James B. Conant, Chairman of the NDRC, assigned Dr. Roger Adams to head a special subcommittee, Section B-9-c, to investigate "Special Problems." On April 1, 1943 this subcommittee was reformed as Division 19, under the direction of H.M. Chadwell, Chief. The official title of Division 19 was "Miscellaneous Weapons."

Throughout its existence, Division 19 received few "special problems" from the Army or Navy. The newly created division limited its activity almost exclusively to problems submitted by the Office of Strategic Services (OSS) and the British liaison officers assigned to that group.

As part of its mission, Division 19 supervised the work of a central research and development laboratory, the Maryland Research Laboratory (MRL), which worked closely with the Research and Development Branch of the OSS. This division called on the other twenty-two divisions, panels, and committees within the NDRC for assistance on problems relating to their specialties. From April 1, 1943 to June 30, 1945 Division 19 expended 2,393,500 US dollars in the research and development of special weapons and devices for the OSS and the British allies.

THE ORGANIZATION OF NDRC

The duties of the National Defense Research Committee were (1) to recommend to the Director of the OSRD suitable projects and research programs on the instrumentalities of warfare, together with contract facilities for carrying out these projects and programs, and (2) to administer the technical and scientific work on the contracts. The NDRC functioned, more specifically, by initiating research projects on requests from the Army or the Navy, or on requests from an allied government transmitted through the Liaison Office of the OSRD, or on its own considered initiative as a result of the experience of its members. Proposals prepared by the division, panel, or committee for research contracts for performance of the work involved with such projects were first reviewed by the NDRC, and if approved, recommended to the Director of the OSRD. Once the Director approved a proposal, a contract permitting the maximum flexibility of scientific effort was arranged.

Originally the NDRC administered its work through five divisions, each headed by one of the NDRC members. These were:

Division A—Armor and Ordnance
Division B—Bombs, Fuels, Gases & Chemical Problems
Division C—Communications and Transportation
Division D—Detection, Controls and Instruments
Division E—Patents and Inventions

In a reorganization in the fall of 1942, twenty-three administrative divisions, panels, or committees were created, each with a chief selected on the basis of this outstanding work in the particular field. The NDRC members then became a reviewing and advisory group to the Director of the OSRD. The final organization was as follows:

Division 1—Ballistic Research
Division 2—Effects of Impact and Explosion
Division 3—Rocket Ordnance
Division 4—Ordnance Accessories
Division 5—New Missiles
Division 6—Subsurface Warfare
Division 7—Fire Control
Division 8—Explosives
Division 9—Chemistry
Division 10—Absorbents and Aerosols
Division 11—Chemical Engineering
Division 12—Transportation
Division 13—Electrical Communication
Division 14—Radar
Division 15—Radio Coordination
Division 16—Optics and Camouflage
Division 17—Physics
Division 18—War Metallurgy
Division 19—Miscellaneous
Applied Mathematics Panel
Applied Psychology Panel
Committee on Propagation
Tropical Deterioration Administrative Committee

SECRET

SE[...]
United States of America

NATIONAL DEFENSE RESEARCH COMMITTEE
1530 P Street NW., Washington, D. C.
Telephone: REpublic 7500

THIS IS TO CERTIFY THAT: LOUIS F. FIESER

Division of Chemistry and

of the Division of Chemical Engineering

is authorized by the Secretary of   War and Navy
(War and or Navy)
in accordance with letters of authorization already furnished
you, to visit and consult with proper officials on matters pertaining to the National Defense on the following subjects: Incendiaries,

Chemical Warfare Munitions.

(Signature of bearer)

Serial No.   9/11.3-2698

Date issued   October 1, 1944

Valid to   April 1, 1945

Chairman, National Defense Research Committee.

Col., GSC   (for the Secretary of war.)

(for the secretary of the Navy.)

D-0990

I.D. Card for the National Defense Research Committee

Photo credit: Cdr. George L. Graveson

General William Donovan (1883–1959)
Won the Medal of Honor in W.W. I as well as his nickname "Wild Bill." In 1941 he was named the COI (Coordinator of Information). A year later the COI became the OSS (Office of Strategic Services). In 1945 President Truman disbanded the OSS. Gen. Donovan added his advice to the establishment of the CIA (Central Intelligence Agency) in 1947.

He was American Ambassador to Thailand (1953–1954) before retiring.

This photograph was presented to Cdr. George L. "Gravy" Graveson, U.S.N. and inscribed to him "with great respect and affection" by Gen. Donovan. Cdr. Graveson was an OSS communications specialist who ended the war in charge of all OSS communications in Europe.

Office of Strategic Services Research and Development Branch History

On 13 June 1942, the Office of Strategic Services (OSS) was established as an operating agency of the US Government under the direction and supervision of the Joint Chiefs of Staff. Among its responsibilities were the progressive and orderly development of operating procedures and the characteristics of special weapons and special equipment for the special operations not assigned, or pertinent to, other US Government agencies. Development of special weapons and special equipment was approved by the Office of Scientific Research and Development (OSRD), and developed jointly with the National Defense Research Committee (NDRC) of the OSRD.

The Research and Development Branch (R&D) of the OSS grew out of the technical development section of the Coordinator of Information (COI). On 17 October 1942, it became an independent branch of the OSS that reported directly to the director of the OSS, Col. William J. Donovan, and the assistant director. OSS R&D maintained this special status throughout the war.

The first director of OSS R&D, Stanley P. Lovell, was selected from the staff of the NDRC by its director, Dr. Vannevar Bush. Because of the close working relationship between the OSS R&D and the NDRC, Lovell remained a special assistant to the head of the OSRD as well as director of OSS R&D.

While other OSS branches, such as Communications, carried out research and development in their specialized fields, R&D maintained the overall function and liaised with the OSRD and Division 19 of the NDRC.

OFFICE OF STRATEGIC SERVICES ORGANIZATION CHART

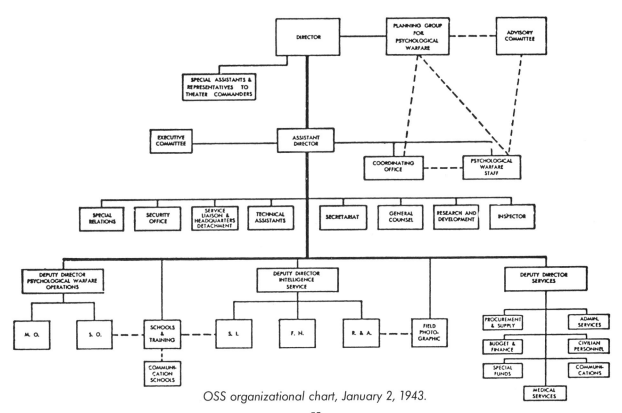

OSS organizational chart, January 2, 1943.

OSS R&D was responsible for:

(1) the special weapons, equipment, and devices necessary for subversive war;
(2) the numerous items necessary to support agent cover;
(3) the camouflage of equipment or devices to facilitate special operations;
(4) the collection and dissemination of information on all types of equipment, whether developed within or without the OSS, which would be of use in OSS operations.

Work projects for OSS R&D were developed in several ways:

(1) R&D in response to, and in support of, problems developed in the field;
(2) anticipation of equipment and special devices likely to be needed in future operations;
(3) from research supplied by, and originating within, the NDRC.

In the fall of 1942 an arrangement was established in which laboratory facilities were made available to the NDRC for the exclusive purpose of developing weapons and devices for the OSS. This unit, designated Division 19 of the NDRC, was supplemented by the establishment of the Maryland Research Laboratory (MRL) to perform the laboratory work. When the requirements for new equipment overtaxed the facilities of MRL, selected universities and laboratories were assigned work on specific projects.

By October of 1943, the organization of the OSS R&D Branch had followed the development of its functions. It consisted of four divisions:

(1) **Technical Division**—While Division 19 of NDRC was tasked with basic research and development, the Technical Division was assigned to see that scientific research did not exceed the limits of operational practicability. The Division assigned a project engineer to follow NDRC developments closely, and to arrange for final testing of devices before the User Trial Committee. This committee was comprised of representatives of the NDRC, MRL, British Liaison Mission, and the OSS Procurement and Supply Branch. All devices intended for Special Operations were coordinated closely with the SOE, in accordance with an OSS/SOE agreement that they be virtually interchangeable in the field.
(2) **Documentation Division**—Established to produce all documents necessary to authenticate agent cover in enemy and enemy-occupied territory, including identity cards, passports, driver's licences, etc.
(3) **Camouflage Division**—Created to camouflage personal accessories and devices and equipment needed for special operations.
(4) **Special Assistants Division**—Formed to provide certain specialized items for agents that did not fall within the purview of the other three divisions for technical or other reasons.

OSS
PRESENTATION

OSS WEAPONS

SPECIAL WEAPONS AND DEVICES
RESEARCH AND DEVELOPMENT BRANCH
OFFICE OF STRATEGIC SERVICES
WASHINGTON   JUNE 1944

OSS Globe Emblem

DESCRIPTION: The high grade steel blade is diamond shaped in cross section from the hilt to the point. The hilt, handle and knob are made of three separate pieces of brass which are assembled securely onto the blade. The Knife is carried in a special scabbard, designed so that it may be worn high or low on the belt. By using one upper and one lower slot the scabbard may be angled into any position, fitted snugly to any part of the body, with ready access to either hand.

PURPOSE: The Fighting Knife is a close combat weapon, excellent for stealthy attack, but is not designed for all-purpose use. It may supplement firearms or be used by the operator as his sole means of defense or offense. The knife is double-edged and can be used for either penetration or cutting.

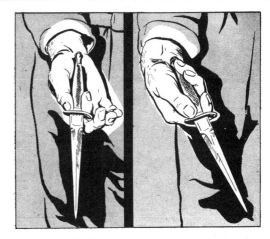

HOLD KNIFE lightly between thumb and next finger, end of handle lying between fatty tissues of palm.

THE FAIRBAIRN SYSTEM is the most widely known technique of knife fighting among American combatants today. It embodies various slashing operations, with aim directed at vulnerable arteries at side of neck, lower center of stomach, h e a r t, below shoulder blade, above wrist, or at armjoint.

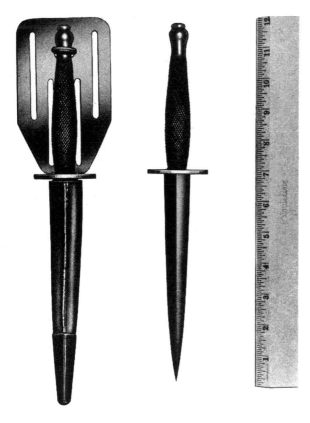

Length of knife only	. . . .	11 1-4"
weight of knife only	. . . .	7 oz.
length in scabbard	. . . .	12 3-8"
weight, in scabbard	. . . .	10 1-2 oz.
packed 6 to a carton		
weight of carton	. . . .	4 lbs. 10 oz.
32 cartons to a case		
shipping weight of case	. . . .	150 lbs
cubage	. . . .	4.5 cu. ft.

SMALL FIGHTING KNIFE*

DESCRIPTION: The 3-4 Fighting-Knife is a smaller version of the issue fighting knife. The high-grade steel blade is double-edged, diamond-shaped, and sharpened to a "needle point." The one-piece brass handle is knurled to prevent slipping. A short, wavy guard provides protection for the fingers. The special leather scabbard features a rubber retention ring and may be strapped to the arm in a variety of positions.

PURPOSE: The Small Fighting Knife is designed to provide a small, but lethal, fighting knife that can be easily concealed. It is designed for close combat and is most effective when used to attack the vital points of the human body. It is not suitable for all-purpose use.

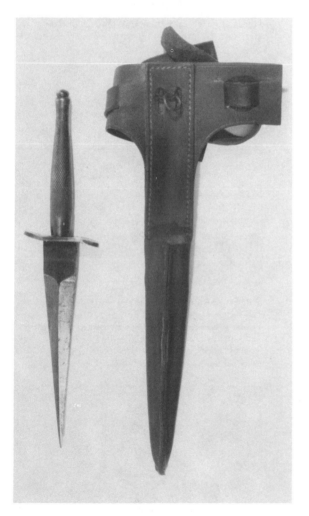

length of knife only . . . . 7 3-4"
length of blade only . . . . 4 1-2"
length of scabbard . . . . 9"

USE OF THE KNIFE: Certain arteries are more vulnerable to attack than others, because of their being nearer the surface of the skin or not being protected by clothing or equipment.

No.	Name of Artery	Size	Depth below Surface in inches	Loss of Consciousness in seconds	Death	
1....	Brachial	Medium	½	14	1½	Min.
2....	Radial	Small	¼	30	2	"
3....	Carotid	Large	1½	5	12	Sec.
4....	Subclavian	Large	2½	2	3½	"
5....	(Heart)	—	3½	Instantaneous	3	"
6....	(Stomach)	—	5	Depending on depth of cut		

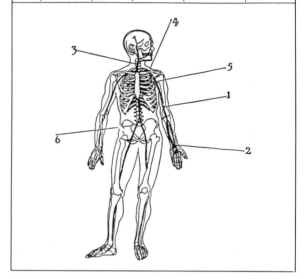

In the diagram the approximate positions of the arteries are given. They vary in size from the thickness of one's thumb to that of an ordinary pencil. Naturally, the speed at which loss of consciousness takes place will depend on the size of the artery cut.

The heart or stomach, when not protected by equipment, should be attacked. The psychological effect of even a slight wound in the stomach is such that it is likely to throw your opponent into confusion.

ISSUED BY: SOE

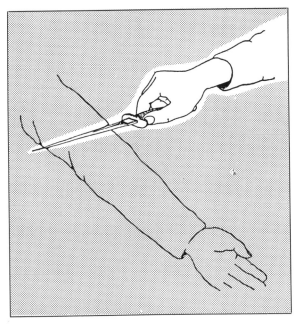

SLASH TO THE INNER ELBOW

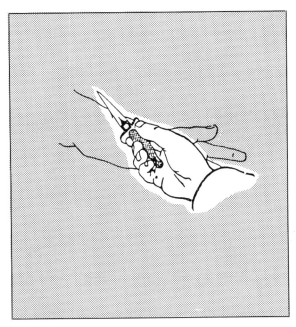

CUT THE TENDONS IN THE WRIST AND FOREARM

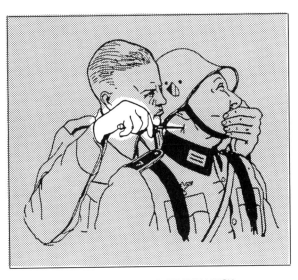

STAB DIRECTLY INTO THE SIDE OF THE NECK

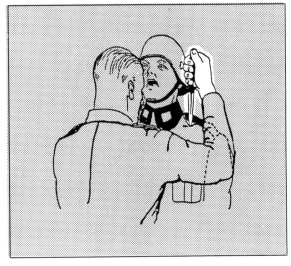

STAB DEEP INTO THE SOFT AREA AT THE SIDE OF THE NECK

SLEEVE DAGGER*

DESCRIPTION: The Sleeve Dagger is a small polished steel dagger with a fitted leather scabbard and strap.

PURPOSE: The Sleeve Dagger is an emergency weapon designed to be strapped to the forearm. It is intended to be used as a thrusting weapon, with the rounded end supported by the base of the palm. It is possible to inflict a lethal wound when the dagger strikes one of the body's vital spots. The Sleeve Dagger is intended to be used at close range when no alternative weapons are available.

```
overall length . . . . . . . . . . . . . . . . . . . . . . 7 5-8"
blade length  . . . . . . . . . . . . . . . . . . . . . 3 3-4"
```

ACTUAL SIZE

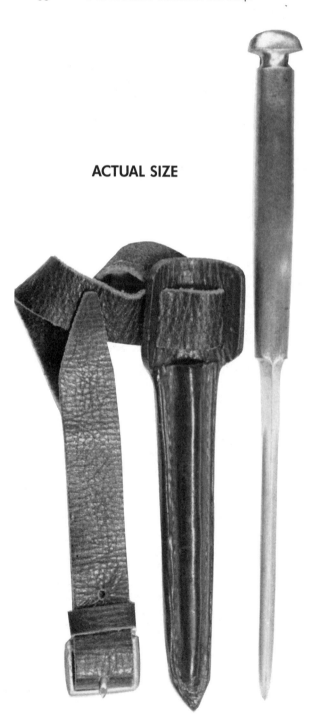

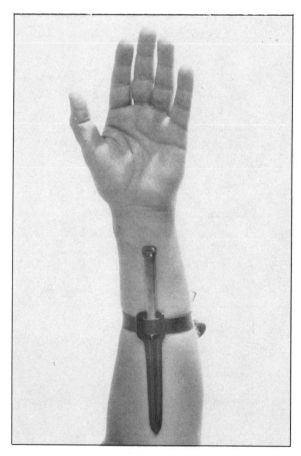

When worn in this manner the Dagger is easily concealed within the sleeve of a shirt or coat.

ISSUED BY: SOE

RESTRICTED

DESCRIPTION: The Lapel Knife is an ultrathin, easily concealed blade in a fitted leather sheath.

PURPOSE: The blade and sheath are intended to be sewn inside the lapel of a jacket, or elsewhere in the clothing. The small size of the lapel knife makes it easy to conceal and difficult to find while being searched. The weapon is most effective when used in a stabbing movement to the face or vital points of an unsuspecting opponent. It is anticipated that the Lapel Knife would be used only in circumstances in which no other weapon is available.

ACTUAL SIZE

length of knife . . . . 3"
width of knife . . . . 19-32"

Sheath available in tan or black leather.
The knife is available in polished, or darkened, nonreflective finish.

USE THE SMALL BLADE TO ATTACK THE
EYES, FACE, NECK, AND THROAT

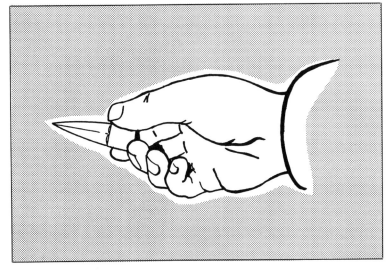

ISSUED BY: SOE

FRISK KNIFE*

DESCRIPTION: The Frisk Knife is a small, thin, double-edged blade with a nonreflective finish.

PURPOSE: The Frisk Knife is designed to be taped flat against the upper arm or lower leg so that it will be overlooked in a preliminary "frisk," or body search. The double-edged blade is intended for use as an emergency weapon at close range. The knife may be thrown, or wielded with a slashing or jabbing movement to the exposed or vital points of the anatomy. The weapon can be very effective when used decisively against an unsuspecting opponent.

length . . . . 7 3-8"
width . . . . .7-8"
thickness . . . . 3-16"

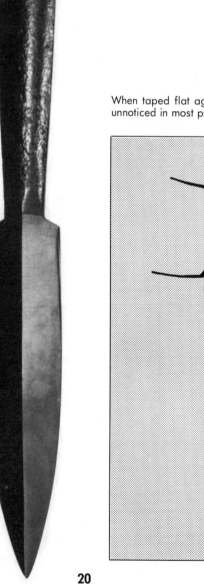

ACTUAL SIZE

When taped flat against the leg, the Frisk Knife will pass unnoticed in most preliminary searches.

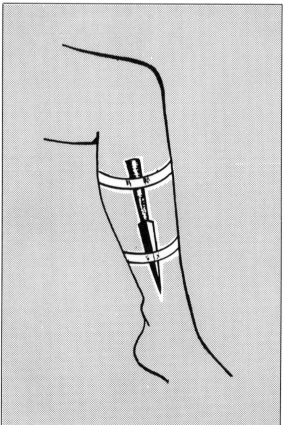

ISSUED BY: OSS

RESTRICTED

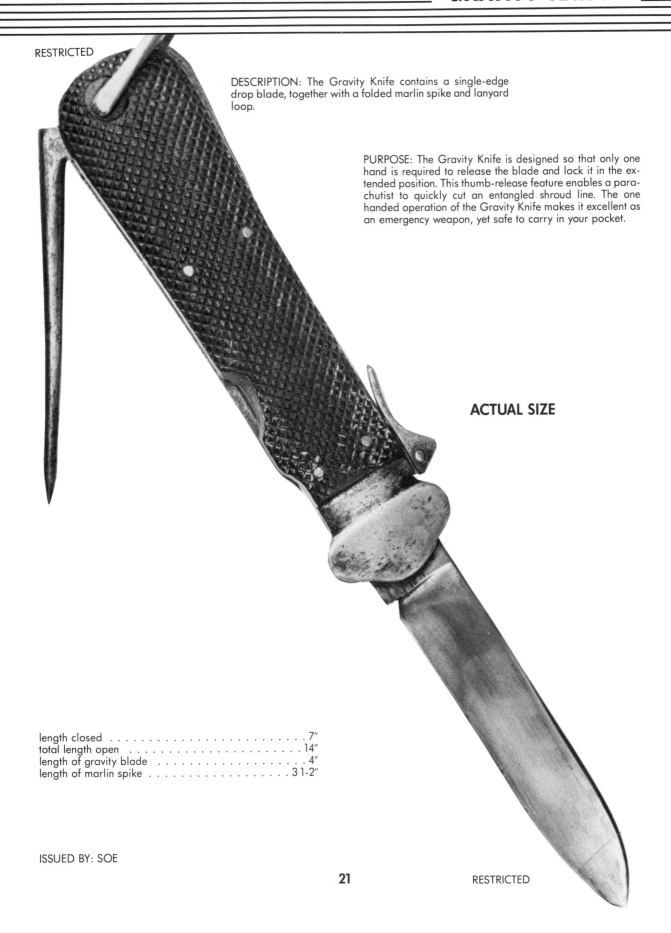

DESCRIPTION: The Gravity Knife contains a single-edge drop blade, together with a folded marlin spike and lanyard loop.

PURPOSE: The Gravity Knife is designed so that only one hand is required to release the blade and lock it in the extended position. This thumb-release feature enables a parachutist to quickly cut an entangled shroud line. The one handed operation of the Gravity Knife makes it excellent as an emergency weapon, yet safe to carry in your pocket.

ACTUAL SIZE

length closed . . . . 7"
total length open . . . . 14"
length of gravity blade . . . . 4"
length of marlin spike . . . . 3 1-2"

ISSUED BY: SOE

RESTRICTED

SMATCHET

DESCRIPTION: The Smatchet is a heavy broad-bladed knife with a high-tempered, high-carbon steel blade and a wooden handle topped by a metal pommel. The blade is sharpened the full length of one edge and half of the other edge. It is sheathed in a leather-covered wood scabbard, fitted with a strap for holding the knife in place at all times, even when the wearer is upside down.

PURPOSE: The Smatchet is a heavy, balanced, close combat weapon, combining the features of the machete and bolo. When properly used it will readily penetrate thin sheets of metal, such as is used in the ordinary steel helmets.

The weapon should be worn so that the user has complete freedom of movement in squatting and climbing. For most users the ideal position of the scabbard is high on the left side (See illustration)

Knots in the leather thong prevent slipping, and the loop fits the wrist securely but may be slipped off easily. The handle is gripped close to the guard, with pommel and cutting edge pointing downward.

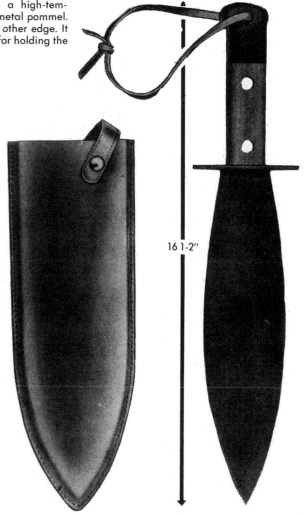

16 1-2"

Length of smatchet	16 1-2"
weight of smatchet only	1 lb. 9 oz.
length in scabbard	17 1-2"
weight, in scabbard	2 lbs. 3 oz.
packed one to a carton	
24 cartons to a case	
shipping weight of case	92 lbs.
cubage	2.8 cu. ft.

WEAR IT HIGH ON LEFT WAIST

ALLOW FOR SLIPPING IT OFF EASILY

KNOT ON TOP, EDGE DOWNWARD

22

METHODS OF USE

CUT AT INNER ELBOW, OR SLASH JUST ABOVE WRIST.

PLUNGE DEEP INTO STOMACH.

SABRE SLASH TO RIGHT OR LEFT LOW ON NECK.

SMASH UP UNDER THE CHIN WITH THE POMMEL.

SPRING COSH

DESCRIPTION: The Cosh is constructed of two heavy concentric springs encased in a tubular steel handle with a leather cover to which a thong is attached. At the end of the smaller spring is a heavy metal knob, which is the chief striking element. When telescoped the Cosh is 7 inches long; fully extended it measures 16 inches.

PURPOSE: The Spring Cosh is used like any club, but it is designed for easy concealment on the person. The Cosh is essentially a plainclothes weapon for a specific mission. It contains the advantage of surprise. As it is swung, two sections emerge from the short tube, extending to a club of sizeable length.

Normally, it is carried concealed up the sleeve of the operator, held so that the head lies in the center of the right palm; the tip shows between thumb and first finger. (See illustration)

weight . . . . 10 oz.
Length . . . . . 7" (closed) 16" (extended) x 1 1-8" diam.

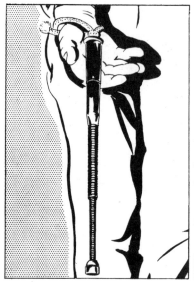

Cord tied to fit wrist securely but to slip off with ease. Knot lies atop wrist.

Ready for action, cosh and cord are up sleeve. Tip shows but is not gripped.

Weapon may be concealed up sleeve or in any other part of clothing.

FOR MAXIMUM STRIKING FORCE, the operator moves his left foot forward, throwing his weight on it, about two feet from his objective. Sudden swinging of the arm causes the knob and spring sections to extend. Blow should be aimed at time arm motion is started downward.

OPERATOR AIMS for temple, swings full from shoulder in fast baseball throw. Fully extended, the Cosh is sufficiently long and flexible so that when swung above the opponent's head from behind, the knob will extend beyond the rim of his helmet and strike him on the face or neck.

GARROTE*

DESCRIPTION: The Garrote is a length of high-strength "piano wire" connected to two small steel handles. The Mark-1 Garrote is issued in a small cloth pouch for ease in concealment.

PURPOSE: The Mark-1 Garrote is a lethal weapon designed to eliminate sentries, quietly. When looped around an enemy's neck and tightened, the garrote will kill silently and quickly. It is most effective in the hands of special forces personnel who are trained in the skills necessary for approaching a sentry from behind without being challenged. Personnel should take care to ensure that they are not carrying a garrote if captured.

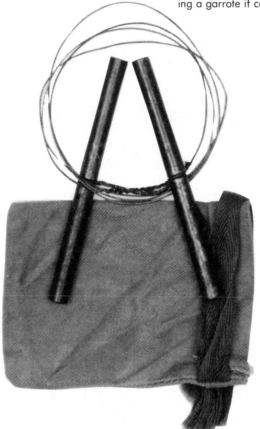

ACTUAL SIZE

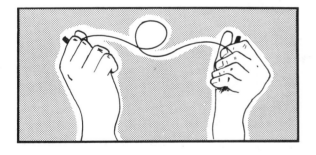

wire length . . . . 24"
handle length . . . . 2 1-2"

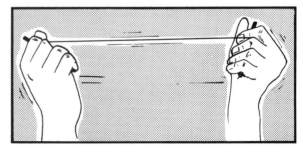

PESKETT CLOSE COMBAT WEAPON*

DESCRIPTION: The body of the Peskett Close Combat Weapon is machined from a single piece of high-grade steel. At one end is a weighted steel ball. Adjacent to this ball is a small ring which is connected to a length of wire which can be extracted from the body of the weapon. A steel button at the opposite end of the weapon is pressed to release a dagger blade that falls and locks into the extended position. The Peskett is issued with a wrist strap and a special belt scabbard.

PURPOSE: The Peskett Close Combat Weapon is an effective multipurpose weapon for combat at close range. The Peskett has the following features:

a) A heavy, weighted, steel ball that makes an effective bludgeon;

ACTUAL SIZE

overall length (closed position) . . . . 7"
length with blade extended . . . . . . 12 1-4"
weighted ball . . . . 1 3-8" diam.
body of Peskett . . . . 7-8" diam.

b) A garrote that can be extracted from the body ot the weapon;

The Peskett Close Combat Weapon is a versatile weapon that allows the user to select one of the three devices available to attack an opponent. It is intended for use by special forces personnel on night operations.

ISSUED BY: SOE

c) A dagger that extends and locks into position from the body of the weapon.

KNUCKLES*

DESCRIPTION: The Knuckles are not brass, but are cast from a special lightweight alloy. The result offers a weapon that is light, strong, and does not rust or tarnish. The flat grey finish on the Knuckles is nonreflective and requires no maintenance. One size will fit most male hands.

PURPOSE: The Knuckles are an effective weapon for hand-to-hand combat. The small size makes it easy to carry in a pocket or clothing. When fitted on the hand, the Knuckles protect the hand from damage and allow the wearer to deliver a crushing blow to an opponent. It is anticipated that they will be carried as a reserve weapon to be utilized for close-in combat.

ACTUAL SIZE

```
length . . . . . . . . . . . . . . . . . . . . . . . . . . . . . 4"
width  . . . . . . . . . . . . . . . . . . . . . . . . . . . . 3-8"
height . . . . . . . . . . . . . . . . . . . . . . . . . . . 2 3-4"
```

WITH THE KNUCKLES you can incapacitate an opponent with a single punch.

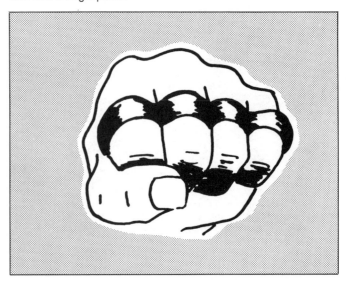

ISSUED BY: SOE

RESTRICTED

DESCRIPTION: The Stinger is a small one-shot .22 caliber weapon, factory loaded, and cannot be reloaded. It can be cocked and fired with one hand. 10 Stingers are packed in a wood and cardboard box sealed in a moisture-proof envelope. Each box contains this pictorial instruction sheet.

PURPOSE: The Stinger is a tiny, easily concealed .22 caliber gun for short range one-shot use. Its extremely small size is an advantage for concealment, and it can be fired from the palm of the hand at a person sitting in a room or passing in a crowd. It is inexpensive, available in large quantities, and can be distributed widely among native patriots of occupied countries.

UNCOCKED

ACTUAL SIZE

COCKED, READY FOR FIRING

Size	. . . .	3 1-4" x 1-2" diam.
weight	. . . . . .	1-3 oz.
packed 10 to a carton		
weight of carton	. . . .	10 oz.
50 cartons to a case		
shipping weight of case	. . . .	49 lbs.
cubage	. . . .	1.6 cu. ft.

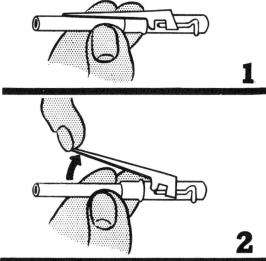

1

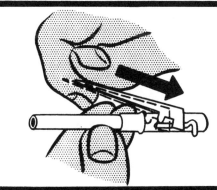

2

3

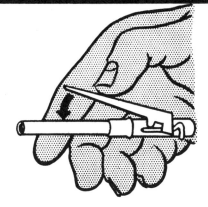

4

5

EN-PEN*

DESCRIPTION: The En-Pen is a single shot, nonreloadable .22 caliber weapon. It has a built-in safety, and a pocket clip that also doubles as a trigger. As shipped, the preloaded En-Pen has a safety clip inserted through the receiver. This clip must be removed for the device to fire. Once the safety clip is removed, a 3-4" rearward movement of the pocket clip will cause a discharge.

PURPOSE: The .22 caliber En-Pen is intended to be used as an emergency weapon. Because it so closely resembles a pocket pen, or mechanical pencil, it may pass unnoticed during a search. Due to its small size and strong recoil, the En-Pen should be held firmly in the hand when firing. It may be concealed and fired safely while seated in a room, or traveling in an automobile. For maximum accuracy and effectiveness, the En-Pen should be fired at very close range.

ACTUAL SIZE

ammunition	.22 caliber
barrel length	3"
overall length	5"
capacity	single shot, nonreloadable

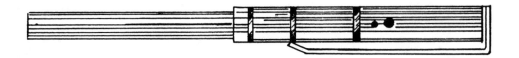

ISSUED BY: SOE

.22 CALIBER CIGARETTE*

DESCRIPTION: The .22 caliber cigarette is a nonreloadable, single-shot firing device. It shoots a 40 grain bullet from a device disguised as a cigarette. The weapon has all of the normal appearance characteristics of a standard cigarette except for weight. When concealed in a standard pack of cigarettes, it is indistinguishable in appearance.

PURPOSE: The weapon is intended for use only as an escape aid when the captive must place his chance of escape on firing one shot. The weapon is intended for use at close range varying from actual contact to eight feet. There is sufficient muzzle energy to inflict a lethal wound with a well placed hit. It must be remembered that only one shot is available, so it must be used to best advantage.

ACTUAL SIZE

Cigarettes are frequently stolen from Allied personnel after capture. Great care should be exercised to avoid loss of this camouflaged firing device!

size . . . . identical to a standard cigarette
weight . . . considerably heavier than a standard cigarette
ammunition . . . . .22 caliber
capacity . . . . single shot, nonreloadable

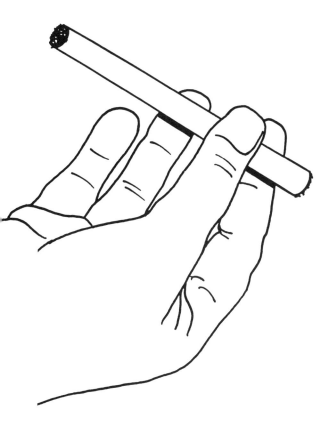

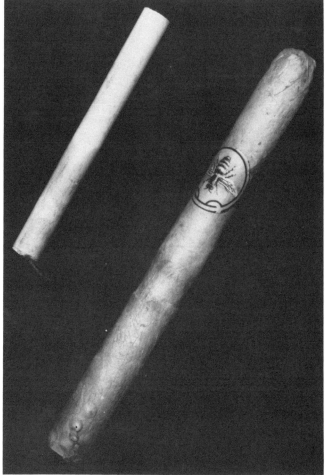

ISSUED BY: OSS

Cigar shown with cigarette for comparative purposes.

PIPE PISTOL*

DESCRIPTION: The Pipe Pistol has the appearance of an everyday smoking pipe. Inside is a single-shot device that fires a .22 caliber projectile through the stem. It is capable of firing only once and is nonreloadable.

PURPOSE: The Pipe Pistol is an emergency weapon designed to be overlooked in an initial search. It is intended to be utilized in situations in which a single shot offers the only chance of escape. The Pipe Pistol is capable of inflicting a lethal wound at a range of up to 10 feet. Because of its extremely short barrel length, it makes a very loud noise on being discharged. This noise and muzzle flash may surprise and confuse the target, aiding in a successful escape.

length	6″
height	2″
width	3-4″
ammunition	.22 caliber
capacity	single shot, nonreloadable

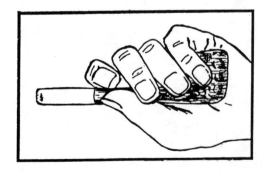

ISSUED BY: OSS

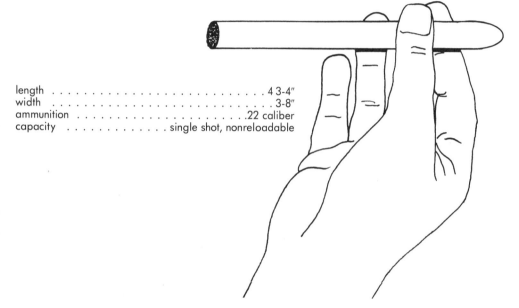

CIGAR PISTOL*

DESCRIPTION: The Cigar Pistol has the appearance of an everyday cigar. Inside, however, is a single shot device that fires a .22 caliber projectile. It is capable of firing only once and is nonreloadable.

PURPOSE: The Cigar Pistol is an emergency weapon designed to be overlooked in an initial search. It is intended to be utilized in situations in which a single shot offers the only chance of escape. The Cigar Pistol is capable of inflicting a lethal wound at a range of up to 12'. Because of its extremely short barrel length, it makes a very loud noise on being discharged. This noise and muzzle flash may surprise and confuse the target, aiding in a successful escape.

```
length  . . . . . . . . . . . . . . . . . . . . . . . . . 4 3-4"
width  . . . . . . . . . . . . . . . . . . . . . . . . . 3-8"
ammunition  . . . . . . . . . . . . . . . . . . . . .22 caliber
capacity  . . . . . . . . . . . . single shot, nonreloadable
```

ACTUAL SIZE

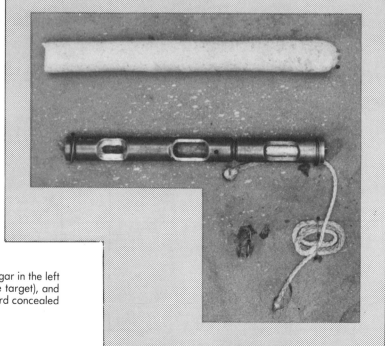

The device is discharged by holding the cigar in the left hand (the lightable end is pointed towards the target), and using the right hand to pull a small length of cord concealed in the rounded end.

ISSUED BY: OSS

LIBERATOR (WOOLWORTH GUN)

DESCRIPTION: The Liberator is a single-shot .45 caliber hand weapon. The operator loads the pistol with a single round by the procedure shown in the accompanying diagram. After the cartridge has been fired it is necessary to push the cartridge case out of the breech by a small stick furnished with the pistol. 10 rounds of standard .45 caliber ball ammunition, which can be carried in the handle of the piece, and a sheet of pictorial instructions are enclosed with the gun in a waterproof carton.

PURPOSE: The use of this gun is primarily for distribution in large numbers among patriots. The construction is very simple and inexpensive. The accompanying instruction sheet is in pictorial form and needs no explanatory text or personal instruction, thus the language and literacy problem is solved. The low accuracy of the pistol and useful range of approximately 25 yards limit it to close-proximity anti-personnel work. Besides its physical use, this weapon, if discovered by the enemy, carries the psychological factor of inducing fear in enemy troops in occupied countries.

Length overall . . . . . 6"
weight with extra ammo. in handle . . . . . 1 lb. 7 oz.
packed 1 to a carton with 10 rounds of ammo.
20 cartons to a case (20 weapons–200 rounds)
shipping weight of case . . . . . 50 lbs.
cubage . . . . . .5 cu. ft.

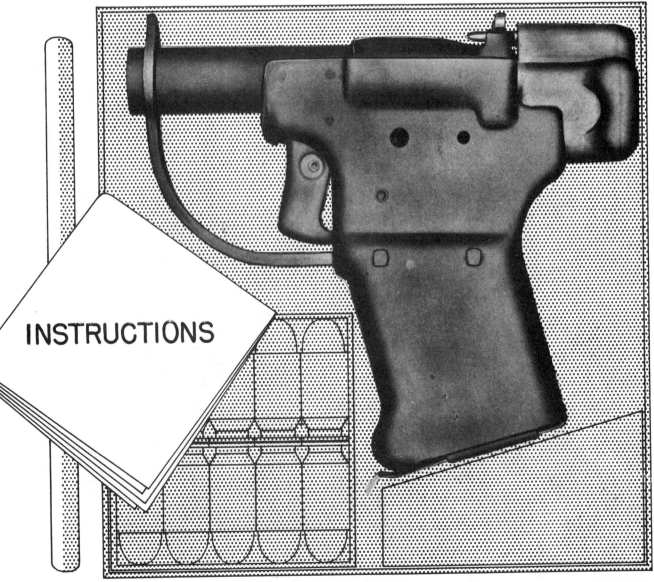

INSTRUCTIONS

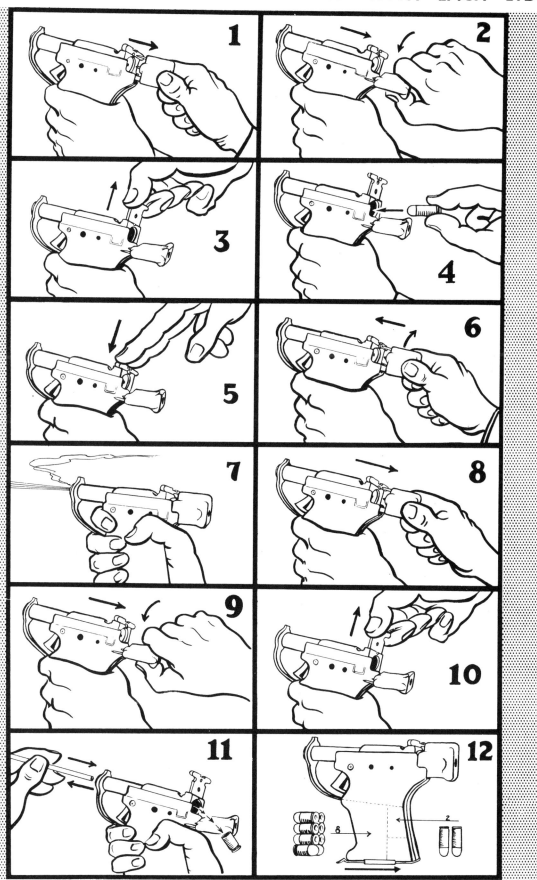

SILENCED .22 CALIBER AUTOMATIC PISTOL

DESCRIPTION: A .22 Caliber Automatic Pistol, clip-fed, carrying 10 rounds of .22 caliber long-rifle high-speed ammunition, with a special silenced barrel. The silencer housing is removable for cleaning purposes only. No rod and patches are to be used. A bristle brush and complete operation and special cleaning instructions are packed with each piece.

PURPOSE: This is an anti-personnel weapon for close range, with noise reduced to a minimum. This 90 per cent noise reduction surpasses that accomplished by any other silencer. The amount of noise audible is merely that of metal contacts and not audible enough to attract attention in normal conditions above traffic noises, doors closing, and other activities of everyday life. This pistol is excellent for use in a closed room or for eliminatng sentries. The muzzle is flashless, even in the dark. The range and accuracy are unaffected and remain the same as of a normal piece.

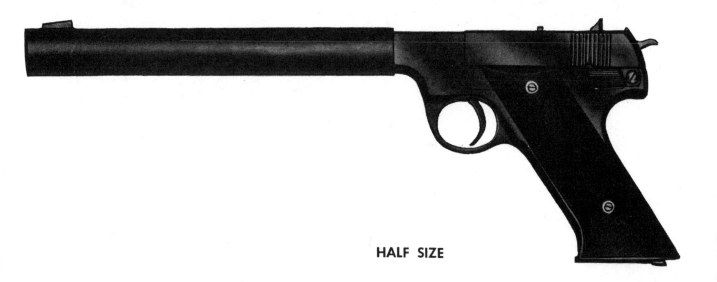

HALF SIZE

length	14" overall
weight	2 lbs. 12 oz.
packed 1 to a carton	
weight of carton with spare screen included	3 1-2 lbs.
15 cartons to a case	
shipping weight of case	75 lbs.

RESTRICTED

DESCRIPTION: The Welrod is a specially constructed, single-shot pistol with a detachable silencer. The weapon is silent, reliable in action, accurate at short range, and easy to conceal.

PURPOSE: The gun is intended for use by specially trained operators for specific tasks. It is accurate up to 50 yards in daylight, or 20 yards on a fairly light night. It is most effective when used with the muzzle against the target.

The gun has three distinct and separate uses:
1) For aimed deliberate shots in daylight or darkness, the effective range of the gun with normal holding is 15–30 yards. With training and practice it is possible to obtain very accurate groups at the distances mentioned. The sights have been painted with a radioactive paint to enable the weapon to be fired effectively in low light conditions.
2) Without its silencer as a single-shot weapon.
3) At the closest quarters, i.e., with the muzzle against the target. The nose cap has been hollowed out so that it can be placed tightly against the body of the target and fired. For this purpose, no special training is required.

```
overall length of gun . . . . . . . . . . . . . . . . . 14 3-8"
maximum depth with magazine . . . . . . . . . . . 5 1-2"
diameter of silencer . . . . . . . . . . . . . . . . . . . 1 3-8"
length of silencer . . . . . . . . . . . . . . . . . . . . . 5"
overall weight . . . . . . . . . . . . . . . . 3 lbs. 6 1-2 ozs.
ammunition . . . . . . . . . available in 9-mm parabellum
capacity . . . . . . . . . . . . . . . . six-round magazine
muzzle velocity . . . . . . . . . . . . . 1000 ft. per second
```

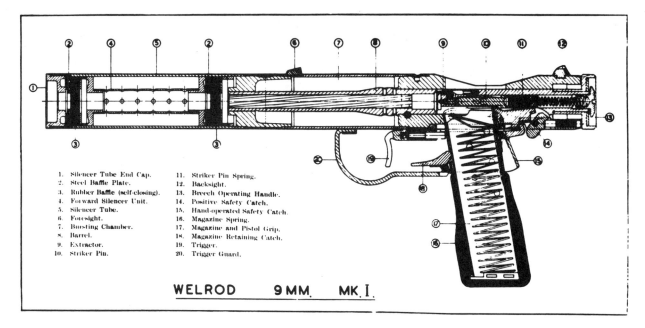

1. Silencer Tube End Cap.	11. Striker Pin Spring.
2. Steel Baffle Plate.	12. Backsight.
3. Rubber Baffle (self-closing).	13. Breech Operating Handle.
4. Forward Silencer Unit.	14. Positive Safety Catch.
5. Silencer Tube.	15. Hand-operated Safety Catch.
6. Foresight.	16. Magazine Spring.
7. Bursting Chamber.	17. Magazine and Pistol Grip.
8. Barrel.	18. Magazine Retaining Catch.
9. Extractor.	19. Trigger.
10. Striker Pin.	20. Trigger Guard.

WELROD   9 MM   MK. I.

ISSUED BY: OSS/SOE

RESTRICTED

GLOVE PISTOL*

DESCRIPTION: The Glove Pistol is a .38 caliber, single-shot firing device mounted on the back of a heavy, leather glove. A trigger bar protrudes from the front of the firing device when the gloved hand is placed in the position of a fist.

PURPOSE: The Glove Pistol is designed to allow ready access to a weapon without the necessity of carrying it in one, or both, hands. The pistol is fired by making a fist, and striking the target. When fired in this manner, the noise of the firing is considerably muted and the need for a bulky silencer is circumvented. In an emergency, the weapon can be fired by tripping the trigger bar with the index finger of the opposite hand. The range of the weapon is five to ten feet.

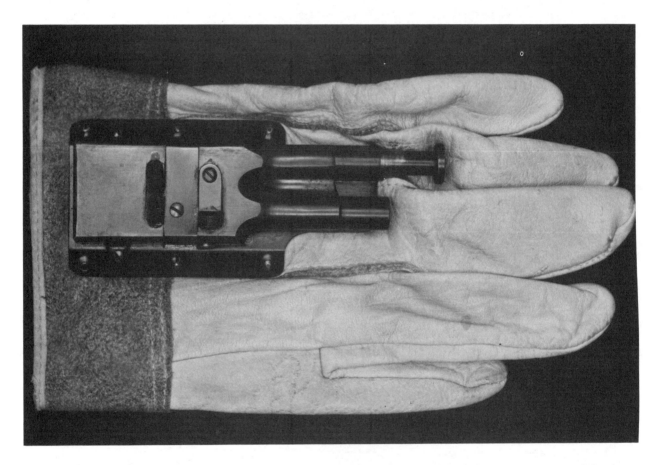

The pistol is intended for use by support as well as special forces personnel.

```
size . . . . . . . . . . . . . . . . . . . . . . . . . . . . large
ammunition . . . . . . . . . . . . . . . . . . .38 caliber S&W
capacity . . . . . . . . . . . . . . . single shot, reloadable
```

ISSUED BY: Office of Naval Intelligence (ONI)

DESCRIPTION: The Belt-Gun is a slightly modified .32 caliber Colt pocket pistol mounted on a web belt, and held in place by a metal retaining bracket. Attached to the metal bracket is a Bowden cable and a trigger-activating lever that allows the gun to be fired remotely.

PURPOSE: The Belt-Gun is designed to be worn inside the jacket on the right side of the waist (barrel pointing forward). The remote activating lever and cable is hidden inside the clothing. The cable extends from the pistol trigger to an activating lever that is worn on a finger ring. When necessary, the thumb is used to activate the lever and fire the gun.

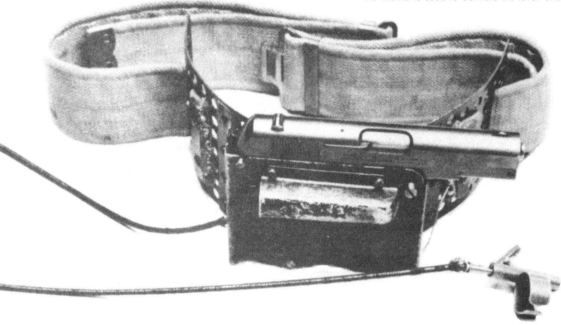

The Belt-Gun is intended to be utilized by personnel operating in civilian clothing in high risk situations. It is intended to be especially effective when fired unexpectedly at close range in situations such as checkpoints, road blocks, etc.

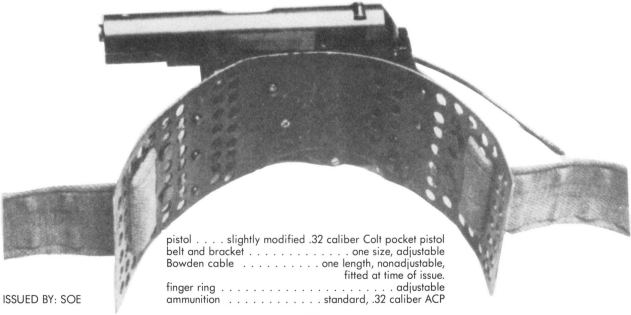

pistol . . . . slightly modified .32 caliber Colt pocket pistol
belt and bracket . . . . one size, adjustable
Bowden cable . . . . one length, nonadjustable, fitted at time of issue.
finger ring . . . . adjustable
ammunition . . . . standard, .32 caliber ACP

ISSUED BY: SOE

.32 CALIBER COLT PISTOL*

DESCRIPTION: The pocket pistol is a .32 caliber Colt automatic. It has a nonreflective finish and features an internal hammer.

A special front "breakaway" leather shoulder holster can be adjusted for varying shoulder widths and body sizes. Two leather ties hang beneath the holster to allow it to be secured to the wearer's belt.

PURPOSE: The .32 caliber Colt automatic pistol can be effectively carried and drawn from within the pocket because there is no exposed hammer to snag on clothing. Its small size makes it ideal for concealment when worn or carried in civilian clothing. The .32 caliber rimless cartridge is most effective when fired at a close range.

```
length overall . . . . . . . . . . . . . . . . . . . . . 6 3-4"
height overall . . . . . . . . . . . . . . . . . . . . . 4 3-8"
ammunition . . . . . . . . . . . . . . . . . . .32 caliber ACP
capacity . . . . . . . . . . . . . . . seven-round magazine
```

The special shoulder holster has been designed to give rapid access to the pocket pistol. The front breakaway design permits the pistol to be drawn from the holster in a forward movement towards the target. The small size of the holster allows it to be worn comfortably for long periods. When worn beneath a suit jacket, or coat, the shoulder holster/pocket pistol combination is undetectable.

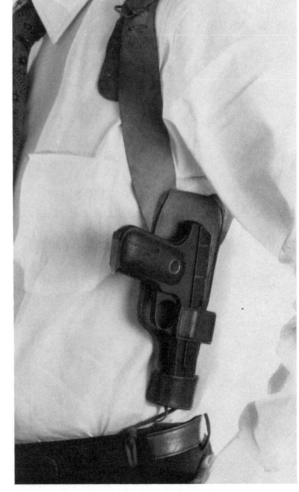

ISSUED BY: OSS/SOE

SILENCED BARREL FOR M3 .45 CAL. SUB-MACHINE GUN

DESCRIPTION: The Silenced Barrel for the M3 .45 Cal. Sub-machine gun is a smooth black metal cylinder 14 1-2" long by 1 1-2" diameter through its thicker portion. The 1 1-2" diameter section contains a screen of fine wire mesh rolled around a perforated barrel lining. The thinner section contains a barrel extension centered through screen discs. The unit is quickly and easily installed in place of the detachable standard 7 1-4" barrel.

PURPOSE: To reduce the muzzle blast of the .45 Cal. Sub-machine gun by cooling the gases and reducing their pressure before release. The perforations in the barrel lining allow the gases to escape behind the bullet and to be retarded and cooled by the wire screens. This process reduces the muzzle noise to approximately the level of the ballistic noise of the bullet, but can not reduce the noise from the mechanical action of the blow-back operated bolt. However, the operator is no longer deafened by the clatter of the piece, even on full automatic fire.

The Silenced M3 .45 Cal. is an extremely effective weapon for wiping out groups of enemy personnel at close quarters, especially indoors. The appreciable noise reduction makes general alarm less immediate and widespread. Experienced operators prefer the feel of the Silenced M3 because the slight extra weight helps keep the muzzle from rising during automatic fire.

The Silenced Barrel requires special cleaning to remove carbon from the screens. The gun will sound louder if not properly cleaned after firing 10 or 15 magazines, or from 300 to 450 rounds. Cleaning instructions and a bristle brush will be shipped with each moisture-proof wrapped Silenced Barrel.

length . . . . 14 1-2"
weight . . . . 1 1-2 lbs.
can be shipped in any number

SNIPER'S RIFLE WITH SILENCER*

DESCRIPTION: The Sniper's Rifle is a specially configured .22 caliber Winchester, Model-74 rifle. The weapon is fitted with a silencer and powerful telescopic sight.

PURPOSE: The Sniper's Rifle is intended to provide special forces personnel with a weapon capable of silently inflicting a lethal wound at a range of up to 100 yards.

```
length without silencer  . . . . . . . . . . . . . . . . . 44"
length with silencer  . . . . . . . . . . . . . . . . . . . 52"
ammunition . . . . . . . . . . . . . . . . . . . . . . .22 LR
magazine capacity  . . . . . . . . . . . . . . . 14 rounds
```

Sniper shown in a concealed firing position.

The target as seen through the telescopic sight.

A weapon that eliminates muzzle flash and muzzle noise offers several advantages to special forces personnel.

(1) The source of the fire is masked.
(2) The location of the weapon firing is difficult for the enemy to pinpoint.
(3) The enemy can not identify the numbers or type(s) of weapons firing, or their range.
(4) The weapon has less recoil and is more accurate to fire.
(5) The enemy is harassed and confused.
(6) The sniper has a psychological advantage over the enemy.

ISSUED BY: SOE

RESTRICTED

DESCRIPTION: The DeLisle Commando Carbine is a spe-cially modified weapon modelled after the Lee-Enfield Mark III rifle. The breech has been altered to accept a .45 caliber cartridge and a modified, 7-cartridge Colt pistol magazine. The weapon features an integral silencer and in-line sights.

PURPOSE: The DeLisle Carbine is designed for use by spe-cial forces personnel who need the capability of eliminating sentries quietly. The weapon is accurate, quiet, and produces no muzzle flash, even on a dark night. At a distance greater than 50 yards the sound is unlike that of a firearm, and is virtually unnoticeable.

overall length	37 1-5"
barrel length	7 1-4"
rifling and twist	6 groove, L.H.
sights	50–200 yards
effective range	275 yards
weight	8 lbs. 4 oz.
ammunition	.45 caliber
magazine capacity	7 rounds
	11 rounds optional

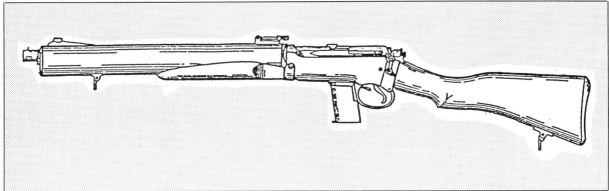

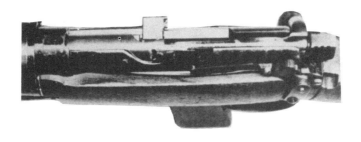

ISSUED BY: SOE

BIGOT*

DESCRIPTION: The Bigot is the combination of a finned projectile and a modified .45 caliber automatic pistol.

PURPOSE: The Bigot is a portable sidearm capable of silently firing a finned projectile with no visible muzzle flash. The projectile is lethal and accurate at a range of up to fifteen feet. The modified .45 caliber automatic pistol is simple to load and fire, and built to provide reliable service in combat. The Bigot is convenient, deadly, and especially useful in night fighting.

length . . . . 6 7-8"
diameter . . . . 13-32"
caliber . . . . .25 cal. projectile charge
pistol . . . . modified to accept conversion unit

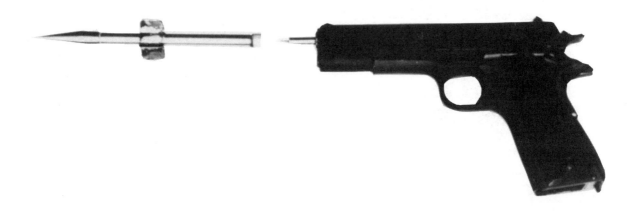

ISSUED BY: OSS

RESTRICTED

DESCRIPTION: The Little Joe is a hand-held crossbow constructed of a special heat-treated aluminum alloy. It uses a rubber propelling unit to fire a wooden dart fitted with a metal broad-arrow point.

PURPOSE: The Little Joe is designed to meet the operational requirements for a silent, flashless weapon capable of inflicting a lethal wound at short range. When fired, the metal tipped dart becomes a flying dagger with razor sharp edges capable of deep penetration into the target. The fired dart strikes with a force many times greater than that of a hand-held dagger.

```
length . . . . . . . . . . . . . . . . . . . . . . . . . . . . 13"
width . . . . . . . . . . . . . . . . . . . . . . . . . . . . . 2"
height . . . . . . . . . . . . . . . . . . . . . . . . . . . . . 8"
weight . . . . . . . . . . . . . . . . . . . . . . . . . 2 1-4 lbs.
```

It is anticipated that the Little Joe will be used by special forces personnel who need the capability of eliminating sentries and guard dogs with a minimum of noise.

The Little Joe fires a one ounce dart at a velocity of 170 feet per second and an accurate lethal range of 30 yards. The extreme range of the weapon is 250 yards. The rubber propelling unit can be used for 60–100 shots before replacement.

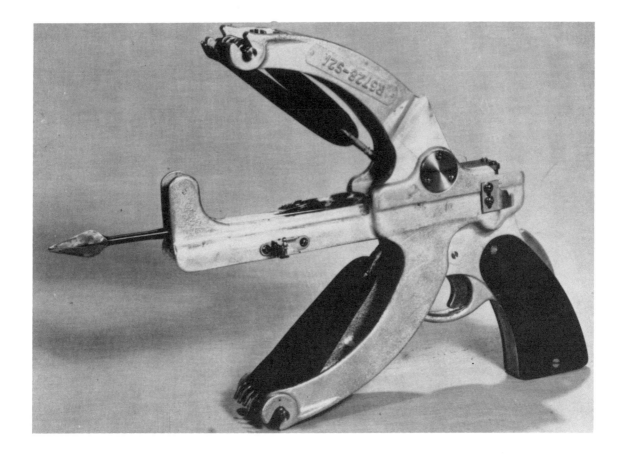

WILLIAM TELL*

DESCRIPTION: The William Tell is a shoulder-fired cross-bow constructed of a specially treated aluminum tubing. It uses a rubber propelling unit to fire an aluminum dart.

PURPOSE: The William Tell is a more powerful crossbow designed to meet the same operational requirements as the Little Joe. It is a silent, flashless weapon capable of inflicting a lethal wound at longer ranges. The pointed metal dart is capable of deep penetration into the target. The shoulder-fired William Tell is a highly accurate weapon.

weight . . . . 3 1-3 lbs.

The William Tell fires a 0.8 oz. dart at a velocity of 180 feet per second. It is anticipated that the William Tell will be used by special forces personnel who need the capability of eliminating sentries and guard dogs with a minimum of noise and at greater ranges and with more accuracy than that provided by the Little Joe.

ISSUED BY: OSS

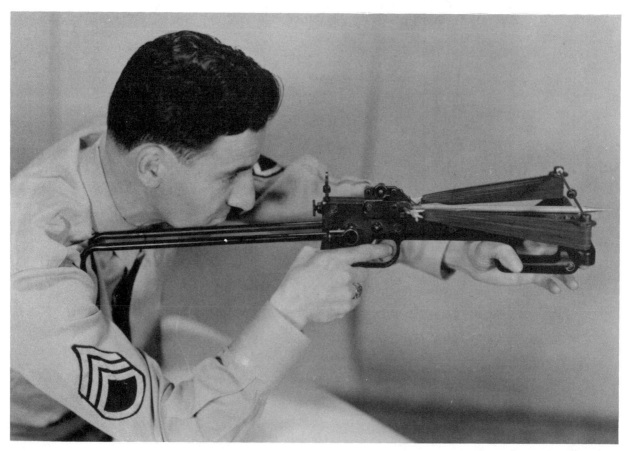

RESTRICTED

DESCRIPTION: The Dart-Pen is the same size and general appearance of a conventional fountain pen. The all metal device uses a powerful spring and compressed air to propel a small "gramophone needle" sized dart.

PURPOSE: The Dart-Pen is readily concealed in the pocket as a conventional writing pen. It is easily aimed, and fires a small dart accurately at a range of up to 40 feet. It can be reloaded and fired again in less than 15 seconds. The Dart-Pen is designed for use as a psychological weapon. It can be utilized to create disturbances and attack the morale of enemy soldiers on public streets, buses or trains.

```
overall length  . . . . . . . . . . . . . . . . . . . . . . . 6 1-16"
barrel length   . . . . . . . . . . . . . . . . . . . . . . . 1 3-8"
capacity . . . . . . . . . . . . . . . single shot, reloadable
```

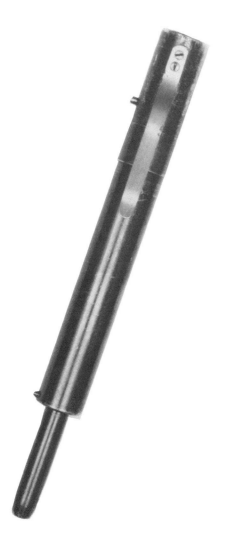

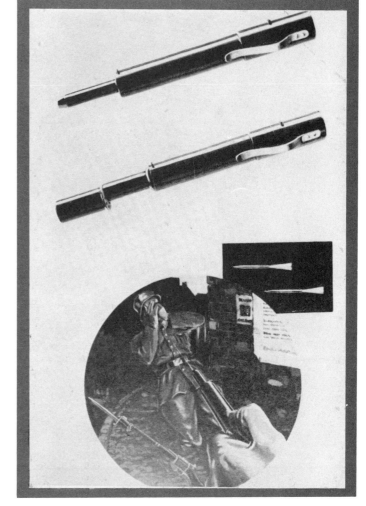

ISSUED BY: MI-9

RESTRICTED

AIR-PEN*

DESCRIPTION: The Air-Pen is a black metal cylinder slightly longer than a conventional fountain pen. Inside the cylinder is a powerful spring capable of firing a dart accurately at a distance of up to 40 feet.

PURPOSE: The Air-Pen possesses a powerful spring that allows it to fire a heavier dart at greater velocities than that of the smaller Dart-Pen. The Air-Pen is fired by holding the body of the pen with one hand, and using the other hand to turn the knurled front ring one-half turn. The Air-Pen is pointed and fired without the use of external sights.

length . . . . 6"
width . . . . 1-2"
capacity . . . . single shot, reloadable

The Air-Pen is intended to be used at night by specially trained personnel to silence guard dogs and larger targets. The Air-Pen may also be employed for psychological warfare against enemy occupation personnel using public transportation or in crowds.

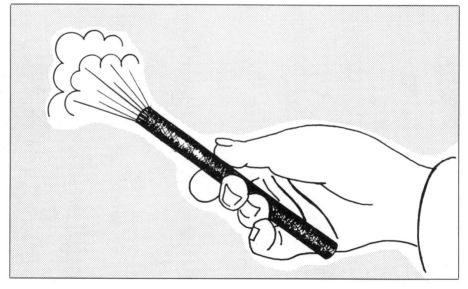

ISSUED BY: SOE

DESCRIPTION: The Pocket Incendiary is a flat black celluloid case filled with a jelled petroleum fuel. Two special Time Delay Pencils are attached to the case for igniting the fuel after the copper-covered glass ampules are crushed. The Time Pencils have colored metal safety strips denoting the time delay period, varying from a few minutes to many hours at room temperature. (See accompanying Time Delay Chart)

PENCIL TIME DELAY CHART

(Tested at 25 C or 77 F)

	Black	Red	White	Green	Yellow	Blue
Average Time	10 min.	19 min.	1 hr. 19 min.	3 hrs. 10 min.	6 hrs. 30 min.	14 hrs. 30 min.

PURPOSE: This incendiary is designed for starting fires at a future time. It is especially useful where a prolonged flame and silent operation are required. It is very effective on lumber piles, in truck cabs, houses, furniture, wheat fields, oil wells, fuel and supply depots, factories and warehouses. The Time Pencils of varying periods allow a great variation of tactical use and give the operator plenty of time to leave the area. The shape of the case allows it to be easily concealed upon the operator's person and when installed. Best operation is obtained when the case is laid on its flat face, but it will create effective fire from any position. Temperature should be considered in selecting the proper time delay pencil. (See Time Delay Chart)

ACTUAL SIZE

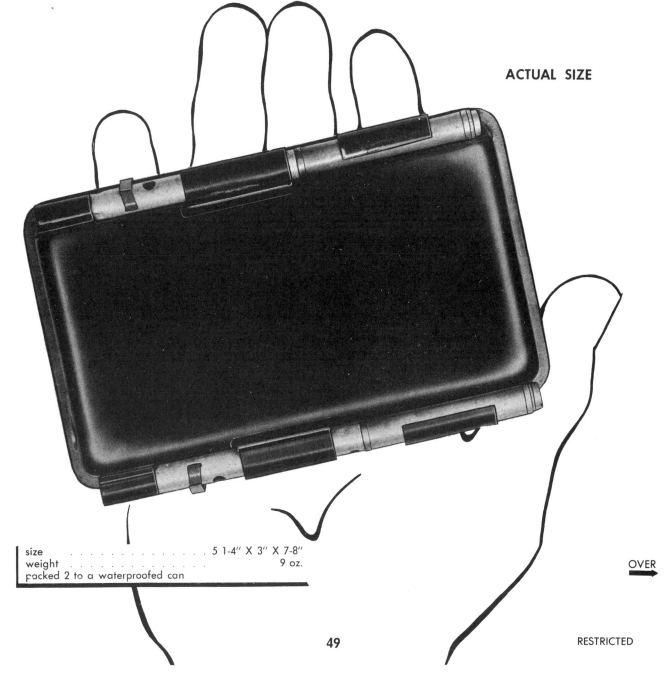

size	. . . .	5 1-4" X 3" X 7-8"
weight	. . . .	9 oz.
packed 2 to a waterproofed can		

OVER →

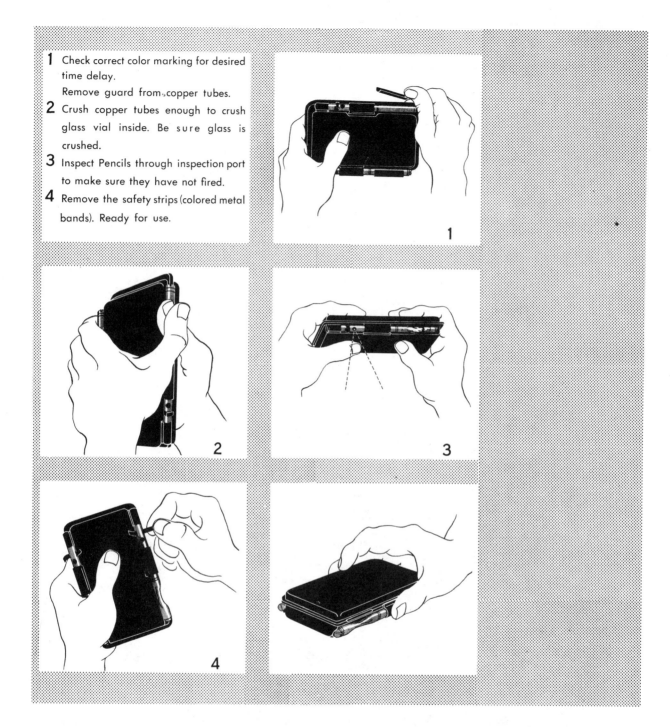

1 Check correct color marking for desired time delay.
Remove guard from copper tubes.

2 Crush copper tubes enough to crush glass vial inside. Be sure glass is crushed.

3 Inspect Pencils through inspection port to make sure they have not fired.

4 Remove the safety strips (colored metal bands). Ready for use.

AFTER SETTING, the corrosive liquid slowly eats the restraining wire. When the wire breaks it releases the striker assembly, igniting the match head. This is followed by a few seconds of intense heat at the ignition tip, which then bursts into flames, igniting the celluloid case and firing the whole incendiary.

IMPORTANT: In order to burn properly, the unit requires access to the oxygen of the air. The user should preferably place the unit between combustible surfaces so that, as the combustion proceeds, the ascending hot air and smoke create a draft, thereby fanning and increasing the fire.

The Time Delay Chart should always be consulted before selecting Pocket Incendiary for a specific job.

DESCRIPTION: The Thermit Well is a plain pasteboard box with a ceramic lining containing Thermit. The ceramic lining has a hole in the bottom sealed by a thin metal tapping plate which prevents the molten mass from dropping through before the chemical action is completed. A graphite orifice plate directs and controls the flow. The box is inclosed in a cardboard sleeve which is adjustable to form a stand for the unit and elevate it about 1" above the surface to be attacked, thus giving the best cutting results. In the recess under the top lid are two short lengths of safety fuse which are fitted into two small fire-wells filled with igniting powder. Also under the lid are two pull-igniters to be attached to the fuses. It is necessary to cut off the waterproofed end of each fuse before attaching the igniters.

size	7 5-8" X 3 3-4" X 2 1-8"
weight	4 lbs.
packed 12 to a carton	

PURPOSE: The Thermit Well destroys metal machinery by cutting through the casing steel (up to 3-4" thick and fusing the gears, pistons, and shafts with a stream of molten iron at 5000 F. It has unlimited uses for attacking and destroying transformers, electric motors, turret lathes and various machine tools in factories, power houses. ships' engines, mines, dock installations, and any mobile machinery. With the use of a ramp of bricks or soft earth the vertical wall of stand tanks, drums, and pipelines can be cut through, causing the contents to flow out. If the liquid is inflammable a fire and explosions will result.

The unit can be easily camouflaged to represent a great many objects such as a simple grocery item or lubricant can.

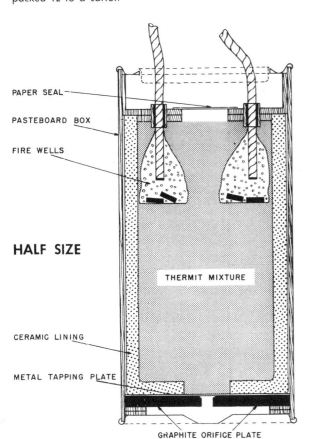

PAPER SEAL

PASTEBOARD BOX

FIRE WELLS

HALF SIZE

THERMIT MIXTURE

CERAMIC LINING

METAL TAPPING PLATE

GRAPHITE ORIFICE PLATE

OVER

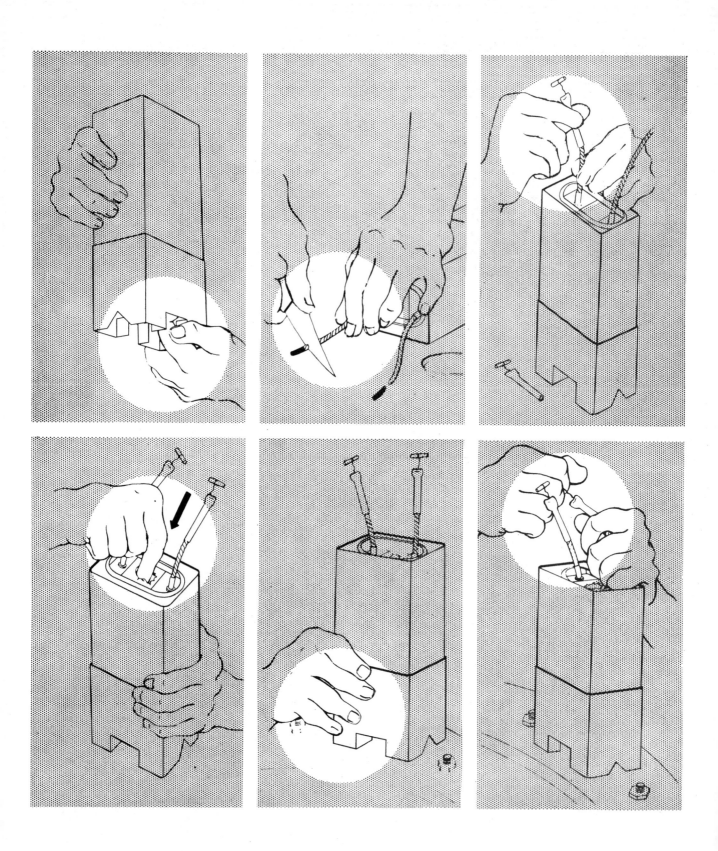

DESCRIPTION: The Small Thermit Well is a plain paste-board box with a ceramic lining containing Thermit. The unit is approximately half the size of the Large Well. The ceramic lining has a hole in the bottom sealed by a thin metal tapping plate which keeps the molten mass from dropping through before the chemical action is completed. A graphite orifice plate directs and controls the flow. An empty space in the bottom of the box insures the correct fall for best cutting results upon the surface to be attacked.

Under the removable top lid is a recess containing one short length of safety fuse and a pull igniter. The fuse leads to a fire-well filled with igniting powder. It is necessary to cut off the waterproofed end of the fuse before attaching the igniter.

PURPOSE: The Small Thermit Well destroys metal machin-ery by cutting through the casing steel (up to 3-8" thick) and fusing the gears, pistons, bearings and shafts with a stream of molten iron at 5000°F. It is planned for attack upon light weight machinery where space or tactical situation prevent the use of the Large Thermit Well. Its small size and simple activating method make it readily camouflaged as a grocery item or lubricant can. It is easily concealed and installed. This Small Well has un-limited uses in factories, power houses, machine shops, or on vehicles. It can destroy transformers, electric motors, lathes, engines, differentials and transmissions. Simple pictorial instructions are packed with each Well.

With the use of a ramp of soft earth or stone (see illustration), the vertical wall of stand tanks, fuel drums, and pipelines can be cut through, causing the contents to flow out. If the liquid is inflammable, fire and explo-sions will result which can destroy a whole supply depot.

size . . . . 4 4-8" X 2 3-8" X 1 3-4"
weight . . . . 14 ozs.
packed 12 to a carton

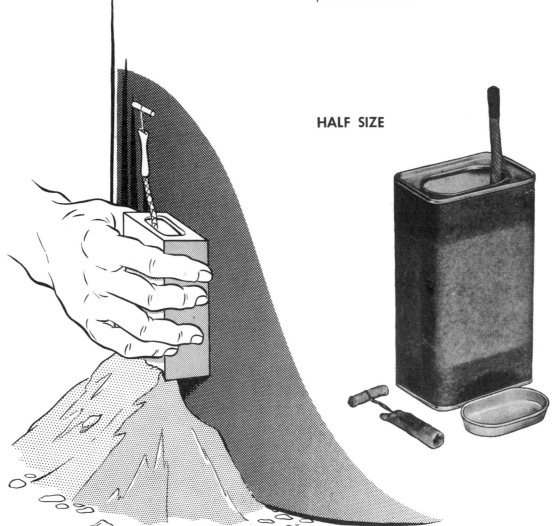

HALF SIZE

OVER →

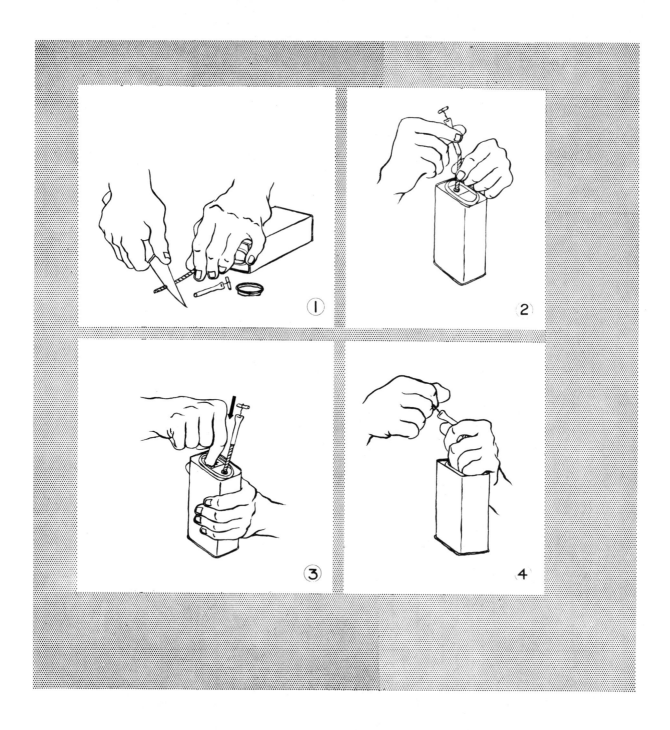

CITY SLICKER (OIL SLICK IGNITER)

DESCRIPTION: The Oil Slick Igniter is a sealed, waterproof cardboard carton, 5 1-2" x 3 3-8" x 2", containing a chemical mixture capable of igniting fuel oil slicks on water. The carton is bound by 2 strips of adhesive for added strength when dropped from a plane. One side of the box has a wax-sealed flap, to be lifted before dropping the Igniter upon the water's surface. Combustion is caused by water entering the opening under the flap and acting upon the chemical contents. There are no pull wires or other mechanical devices. It can be activated only by water. (Tests are now being made to determine the possible advantages of a wedge or pie shaped container.)

PURPOSE: To ignite fuel oil slicks on water. This is an especially useful item for patrol and torpedo bombers, which can drop several on the oil slick of a damaged or crippled enemy vessel. The small carton floats upon the surface and takes about one minute to ignite. It then burns with an intense heat and ignites the oil slick.

Individual operators can well use the Igniter in harbors, rivers or any accessible location of enemy shipping. It could be used in conjunction with or to divert attention from operations with the Limpet or other weapons.

The Oil Slick Igniter is perfectly safe until water-fused.

It may be safely stored in a climate of tropical humidity for at least 6 months, but may lose its activating ability if held longer.

size . . . . 5 1-2" x 3 3-8" x 2"
weight . . . . 1 lb. 4 1-2 oz.

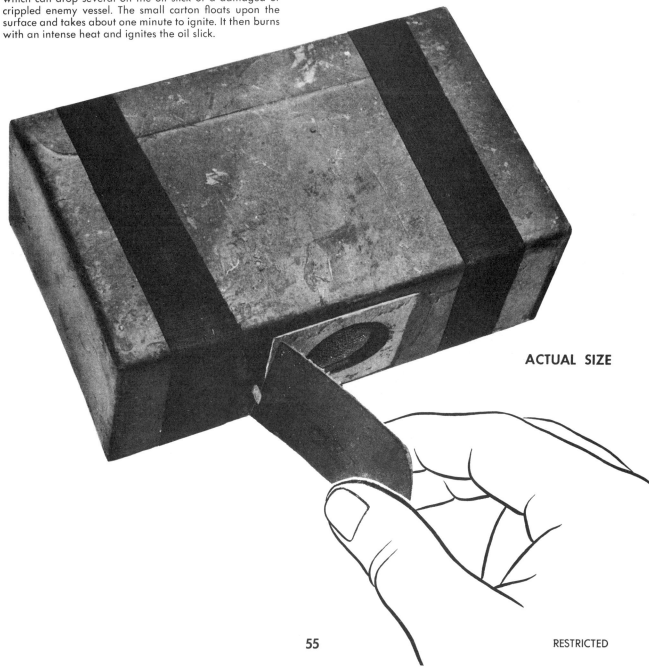

ACTUAL SIZE

INCENDIARY PACKET

DESCRIPTION: The Incendiary Packet is a pocket-size, olive drab metal box with a hinged lid. It contains three small cartons of chemicals. One carton contains powdered potassium chlorate; the second, powdered sugar; the third, thin ampules of sulfuric acid, 2 3-4" long x 1-4" diameter, sometimes referred to as "cigarets." The glass ampules of acid have an outer plastic covering. The carton contains 10 ampules packed in a neutralizing powder to prevent fire from accidental breakage. The outer metal box is sealed by adhesive tape with folded edge for easy stripping.

PURPOSE: By a mixture of chemicals, to cause a vigorous fire at an approximately determined future time. The chemicals will flare up with a brief, extremely hot flame that is capable of igniting any combustible material, indoors or out in the open. This device is primarily a delayed igniter and to be fully effective must be installed where is has combustible material to kindle. In this way it has unlimited uses in attack upon materials in storage places, such as fuel or supply depots. It can also be unobtrusively left where it will ignite woodwork, upholstery, draperies and furniture in offices and dwellings.

The operator mixes small equal portions of the potassium chlorate and the sugar in or under any convenient combustible material. Two or more sulfuric acid ampules are then crushed and inserted into the pile of mixed powders. Care should be taken in crushing the cigarets to break the glass ampules but not the outer plastic. The acid will eat through the plastic and ignite the powders after a minimum delay of 1 hour. The thickness of the cellulose covering determines the length of time before combustion. The time delay period is shorter at warm temperatures and longer at cold temperatures. The boxes of powders contain enough for a maximum of five operations.

The small carton of sulfuric acid ampules in each Incendiary Packet contains five green colored cigarets and five tan colored cigarets. The green ones have a thicker plastic covering and maintain a slightly longer time delay before ignition. The tan cigarets cause a delay of from 1 to 3 hrs., and the green of from 2 to 4 hrs.

A camouflaged means of using the Incendiary Packet is to saturate a piece of clothing or cloth with a water solution of the powders. Allow the cloth to dry and, at the spot of installation, wrap it around several crushed cigarets. When the acid eats through the plastic it will ignite the cloth.

size of packet . . . . 31-4" x 61-8" x 11-8"
weight . . . . 11 1-2 oz.

HALF SIZE

DESCRIPTION: Capsules H are small plastic capsules containing a mixture of powdered potassium chlorate and powdered sugar weighted with buck-shot. The Capsules are constructed of two separate thicknesses of plastic. Overall size is approximately 5-8" x 1-4" diameter.

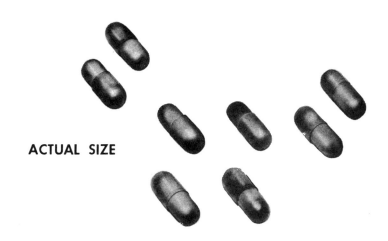

ACTUAL SIZE

PURPOSE: To cause a fire to be ignited by chemical reaction after a time delay. Only part of the necessary chemicals are furnished in the Capsules H for extreme economy of size and time. The other necessary ingredient is sulfuric acid which will take about 2 hrs. to eat through the plastic capsules and ignite the powders. The operator will find this acid in his own or enemy sources of supply. It may be found in regular storage batteries if not available elsewhere.

The best method of improvising a highly effective incendiary is to place a small amount of the liquid acid in a medium sized bottle, drop in two or more Capsules H, and fill the bottle with gasoline or other inflammable liquid, such as half gas and half oil. Inverting the bottle so that the acid and capsules are concentrated in the neck (See illustration) insures efficiency. The acid will eat through the plastic capsules, igniting the powders with a brief hot flame. The bursting bottle will disperse the flaming gasoline. This incendiary is an igniter and should be placed where it will quickly spread to any highly combustible material.

size of capsules	. . . . .	5-8" x 1-4" diameter
packed 150 capsules to a metal container		
weight of container	. . . . .	1 lb. 3 oz.
58 containers to a case		
shipping weight of case	. . . . .	67 lbs.
cubage	. . . . .	1.1 cu. ft.

LIMPET

DESCRIPTION: The Limpet is a waterproof plastic case to contain a high explosive charge. It is equipped with strong magnets for adhesion to the steel plate of merchant vessels. A keeper plate protects the magnets of two Limpets packed face to face. Each end of the plastic case is threaded to receive a waterproof AC Time Delay detonator with safety pin and thumb screw. (See separate listing – AC Time Delay). An accompanying placing rod fits a bracket on the case to aid under-water installation.

PURPOSE: The Limpet is an explosive weapon designed to blow a hole of about 25 square feet in the steel plate of a merchant vessel below the waterline. The attached holding magnets will withstand water pressure caused by the vessel in motion. The best target is near the boilers, which are usually amidships.

The AC Time Delay detonator provides a wide range of delays for the operator's choice to fit the tactical mission. By pre-installing the correct color ampule in the detonator he can vary the delay from a few hours to several days. The following chart is enclosed in each package of AC Time Delay detonators:

TEMP.	RED HOURS	ORANGE HOURS	YELLOW HOURS	GREEN HOURS	BLUE HOURS	VIOLET DAYS	TEMP.
40°F.	6½	9½	20	34	67	8½	5°C.
50°F.	5	8½	17	30	53	7	10°C.
60°F.	4½	7½	15	26	42	5½	15°C.
68°F.	4	7	14	22½	36	4½	20°C.
77°F	3½	6½	12	20	30	3½	25°C.
88°F.	3	6	10	17½	25	2½	30°C.

NOTE: Subject to 15% deviation either way, except Red on which deviation may be 2 hours either way.

For further details and other suggested uses see separate listing under Time Delays.

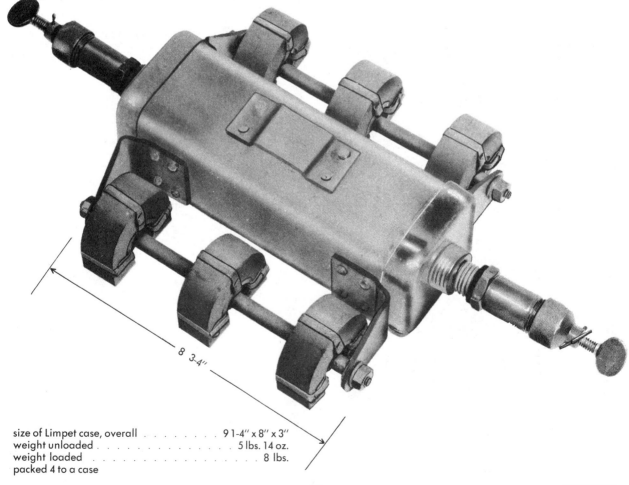

size of Limpet case, overall . . . . 9 1-4" x 8" x 3"
weight unloaded . . . . 5 lbs. 14 oz.
weight loaded . . . . 8 lbs.
packed 4 to a case

Before installation the operator inserts the correct time delay ampules, removes the safety pins and turns the thumb screws crushing the ampules. The Limpet is then attached to the plates of the enemy vessel at least five feet blow the waterline. If the operator has to swim to the target, carrying or towing the Limpet, he should not turn the thumb screws until after the weapon is in place on the ship's plates.

When installation is made from a small boat the operator uses an extendable placing rod, which fits into a bracket on the Limpet case. He may also use a Magnetic Holdfast for a steadying grip on the smooth surface of the ship's hull and to resist the sweep of current or tide. The Holdfast is a Limpet accessory which consists of 8 magnets on a metal frame with a rope handle. If applied above the waterline it must be removed when Limpet installation is completed.

The Limpet may also be initiated by the Mechanical Clock Firing Device, Mark 3, with special Limpet adapter and booster. (See separate listing under Firing Devices.) When a specific time delay is needed to fit known sailing schedules, effective harbor or river block operations may be achieved or simultaneous explosions planned.

The Limpet cases can be requisitioned empty, to be loaded in the field with P.E., or they can be requisitioned already loaded with Torpex. If shipped empty the cases contain a tube of liquid for sealing the removable end cap. After loading with P.E. the Limpet cases must be used within 5 days, due to the possible action of the explosive composition upon the plastic case if stored longer.

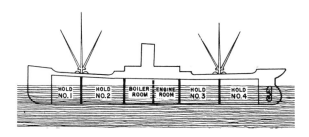

Special packing and shipping arrangements can be specified. Wrenches for making the AC. Delays water-tight are included with the cases. A placing rod is being developed and will be included in the shipment. Accessories, besides the Magnetic Holdfast and placing rods referred to, will in the near future include sympathetic detonators to replace one AC. Delay in multiple installations. However, no detonators or boosters of any kind will be shipped unless specified.

PIN-UP GIRL (LIMPET WITH PINNING DEVICE)

DESCRIPTION: The Pin-Up Girl is a Limpet H. E. charge container without magnets. It is attached to the plates or planking of an enemy vessel's hull by a cartridge-driven pinning device. The cartridge fits into a metal bracket on the case.

The plastic case for the explosive charge has extending brackets or arms for aid in holding the unit flush on the surface of the hull while firing the cartridge. The pinning device is factory-loaded and sealed for under-water use. The pin will penetrate thick steel plating, making the unit practically irremovable even if detected. The explosive charge is activated by two AC Time Delay detonators, one projecting from each end. A wide selective range of time delays is possible by use of different colored ampules. (See AC Time Delays under separate listing.)

PURPOSE: The Pin-Up Girl is a high explosive weapon for destroying enemy merchant vessels. It is a Limpet body with the same H. E. charge. Like the magnetic Limpet, it will blow a hole about 25 square feet in the hull. It is held in position rigidly and immovably by a heavy steel pin which is cartridge-driven through the plates. It can be readily used on wooden hulls where Limpet magnets would not hold.

The pinning device is factory-loaded and sealed for under-water use. It is fired by removing a safety pin and pulling a string to displace the firing yoke, releasing the firing pin. The noise and percussion of the pinning device are unnoticeable to the crew inside the hull. The cartridge for use on wooden hulls has a special pin and is marked with a green band on the cartridge body.

General charactistics of the Limpet apply to the Pin-Up Girl. It should be attached at least 5' below the water-line, and as near the boilers as possible, which are generally amidships. More than one device increases effectiveness of demolition. The charge cases will be shipped loaded with Torpex.

ACTUAL SIZE

PINNING DEVICE

size	5 1-4" x 1" diam.
weight	8 oz.

EXPLOSIVE CASE WITH BRACKET

size	9 3-8" x 6 1-2" x 3"
weight (loaded)	5 1-2 lbs.

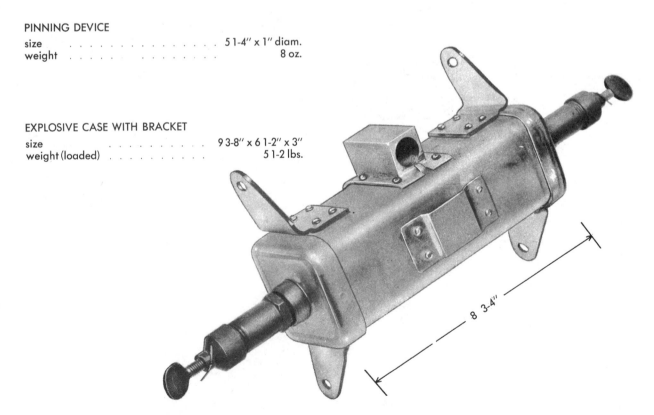

8 3-4"

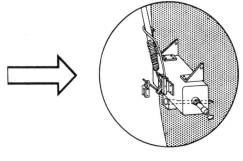

The Pin-Up Girl may be applied from a small boat or by an operator swimming under water. Special care and study should be used in applying the device and firing the cartridge.

Special packing and shipping arrangements of the necessary items and accessories can be specified. Wrenches for making the A. C. Delays water-tight are included with the cases. A supply of placing rods will also be included.

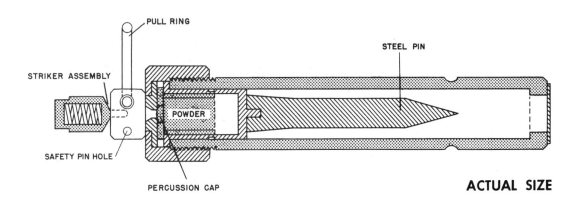

ACTUAL SIZE

CLAM

DESCRIPTION: The Clam is a small compact black plastic case to contain a high explosive charge. It is set off by two Time Delay Pencils. Four strong magnets are built into the box for quickly attaching the unit to any iron or steel surface to be destroyed.

PURPOSE: The Clam is an explosive charge quickly applied to destroy automobiles, trucks, light tanks and small boats. The Clam can be placed on iron or steel surfaces, and will adhere firmly to moving vehicles. Good locations are engine heads, transmissions, and under gas tanks. Placed under the dash of a car or truck it will eliminate the enemy personnel as well as the vehicle. It can also be used in factories under transformers, electric motors, or any metal parts of light machinery. (For demolition of heavier machinery see THERMIT WELL.)

Clams are packaged in units of two, with the magnets face to face. Separating the magnets are keepers, one of which can be used as a screw driver in removing the cover of the case to load with plastic explosive, and to tighten the small recessed set-screws which hold the Pencils securely in the case. Clams are shipped without Pencils.

When only one Clam is used the magnets of the second should be protected by replacing the keepers. Care should be taken to prevent the magnets from striking together or against any other hard surface.

size	6″ x 2 3-4″ x 1 3-8″
weight, empty (will hold approx. 1-2 lb. of P. E.)	13 oz.
packed 50 to a case	
shipping weight of case	57 lbs.
cubage	1.8 cu. ft.

ACTUAL SIZE

The Pencils, requisitioned separately or drawn from local stores, are marked in six different colors. Each color indicates a different delay period. The operator should check the Time Delay Chart for the correct colored Pencil for the job.

TIME DELAY PENCILS
(Tested at 25°C—77°F)

	BLACK	RED	WHITE	GREEN	YELLOW	BLUE
Average Time	10 min.	19 min.	1 hr. 19 min.	3 hrs. 10 min.	6 hrs. 30 min.	14 hrs. 30 min.

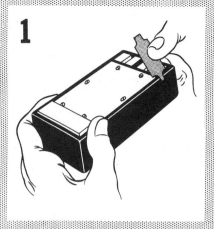

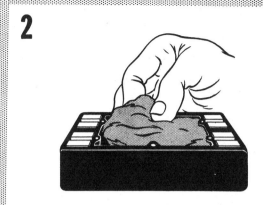

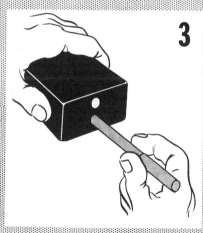

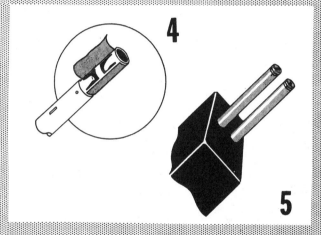

1. BEFORE CARRYING TO INSTALLATION: Remove keepers; use the shaped one to unscrew base plate of case.

2. Pack case with plastic explosive. Replace base plate and screws.

3. Make space for Pencils with wooden rod.

4. Insert detonators in Pencils and wrap snouts with one turn of tape to keep plastic explosive out of detonators.

5. AT JOB: Remove the colored metal safety strips. Insert Pencils through the openings, snout end first. Tighten set screws with shaped keeper plate.

6. Squeeze copper tubes. Be sure inner glass vials are broken.

FOG SIGNAL

DESCRIPTION: The Fog Signal is a small unit to be clamped to a railroad track, resembling a similar item of actual railroad equipment. It contains three percussion caps and loose black powder. A spring snout is fixed to one side for attaching a detonating cap and Primacord. A lead strap fits securely over the rail.

PURPOSE: The Fog Signal is used to set off a charge of high explosive for the demolition of locomotives and trains, tracks, and other right of way structures. It is activated by the wheels of the first truck of a locomotive or car passing over it.

The operator fixes the Fog Signal on the rail with the lead strap. The spring snout must point toward the outside of the track so that the flange of the locomotive wheel will not sever the Primacord. A detonating cap and Primacord are attached, leading to the buried charge. The charge is to be of a size and type selected by the operator as best suited for the job. The charge is placed where it will do the most damage to the rails and rolling stock.

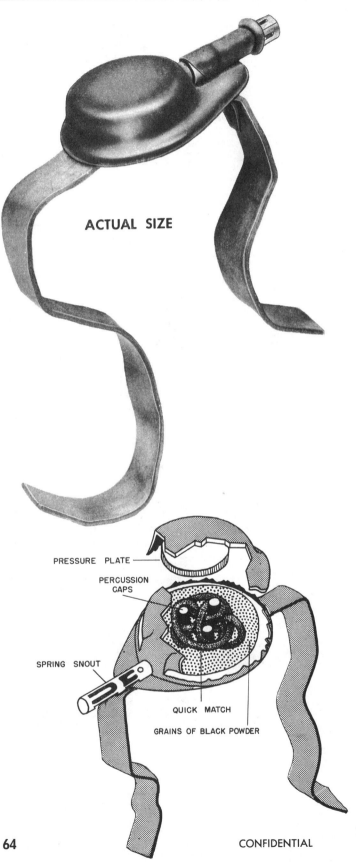

ACTUAL SIZE

PRESSURE PLATE

PERCUSSION CAPS

SPRING SNOUT

QUICK MATCH

GRAINS OF BLACK POWDER

size	2″ x 1 1-2″ x 1-2″
weight	2 1-4 oz.
packed 4 to a metal container	
weight of container	11 oz.
125 containers to a case	
shipping weight of case	100 lbs.
cubage	2.2 cu. ft.

DESCRIPTION: The Mole is a small box-like package, with a safety pin for arming. Two wires lead from one end to a light-sensitive "eye," or photo-cell. This photo-cell unit has two built-in magnets for ahhesion to iron and steel surfaces. The magnets are protected by keeper plates until application. Emerging from the same end of the box are two wires for attaching a special electric detonator. This is inserted into, and will set off, a charge of plastic explosive, TNT, or dynamite. Primacord can be used to carry the detonation to auxiliary charges strategically placed.

Initial activation of the equipment is caused by the sudden and complete shutting off of all light to the photo-cell. Slow changes of light do not effect it, such as transition from day to night. When the photo-cell is activated it sets off the special electric detonator, carrying through to the final H. E. charges.

PURPOSE: The Mole is designed for the special purpose of derailing and destroying an enemy railroad train after it enters a tunnel. Its aim is to completely destroy equipment, and seriously block traffic and service for a long period. Middle European railroads run through many tunnels that can be effectively used to destroy enemy lines of supply and troop movement.

The Mole is specially designed to be effective and unnoticeable on the under-structure of European-type railroad cars. There are many ways it can be applied for cutting axles and wheels, breaking couplings, and for aimed derailment. The purpose is not merely to damage one car, but to cause a total wreck of the entire train inside the tunnel.

Much of the preparation can be done in advance, decreasing time of installation and increasing efficiency of demolition. Careful study by the operator will lead to many efficient ways to attack specific problems.

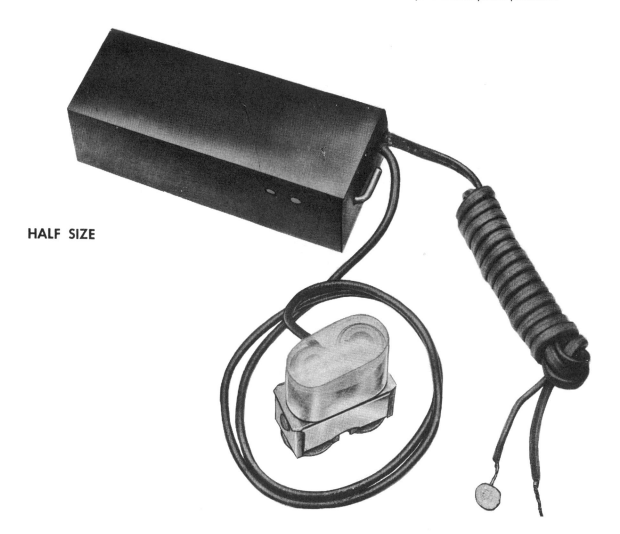

HALF SIZE

OVER →

GENERAL INSTRUCTIONS

To insure a complete wreck it is necessary to shatter at least one front wheel of a car, and to cut the coupling at the forward end. This can be done with two charges activated by the same Mole. If the direction of travel of a car is not known at the installation opportunity, charges can be placed which will cut both couplings and shatter wheels at both ends of the car. These charges should be connected with Primacord for simultaneous detonation.

The function of the Mole is to send an electric current through the detonator about 5 to 10 seconds after the car bearing the Mole has entered a tunnel.

There are two essential conditions for the Mole to become alert:

a. The safety pin must be removed at time of installation.

b. The photo-cell unit must receive some daylight. It must be in a position where it "sees" a well lighted part of the roadbed. The Mole therefore is not alert at night, but will become alert sometime after daylight.

When alert, the Mole will fire the detonator only when suddenly deprived of light, as when entering a tunnel. It will not fire the detonator as the light slowly fades, as at evening.

DESCRIPTION: The Anerometer is composed of three parts packaged together in a metal container. The parts are: 1. The triggering mechanism; 2. The booster; 3. The flexible container for the high explosive charge. This will hold 1 lb. of P. E. (plastic explosive). It is shipped empty.

The assembled unit is 1 1-2" in diameter x 17" long, and partly flexible. It is armed by the removal of an arming strip and a safety pin. The strip serves as a screwdriver for tightening a screw which seals a pressure chamber. The safety pin cannot be removed if the device is unsafe.

PURPOSE: The Anerometer is an explosive weapon designed to be concealed in enemy aircraft while on the ground. It will cause a seriously destructive explosion when the plane reaches an altitude of approximatly 1500 ft. above take-off level.

The explosive charge is sufficient to destroy a wing or tail assembly on large heavy craft, and to cause medium and light craft to disintegrate completely in mid-air. Its internal explosive effect is greater than that of a direct hit by a 75 mm. shell. Properly placed it will cause either total destruction or elimination of personnel and damage sufficient to result in loss of control and a crash.

size	6" x 1 1-2" diam.
fabric container for explosive	12" long
weight without explosive	7 oz.
packed one to a can with booster	

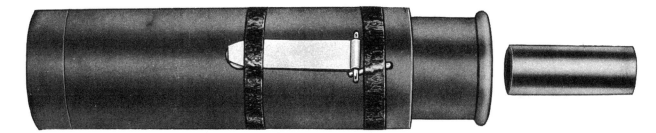

ACTUAL SIZE

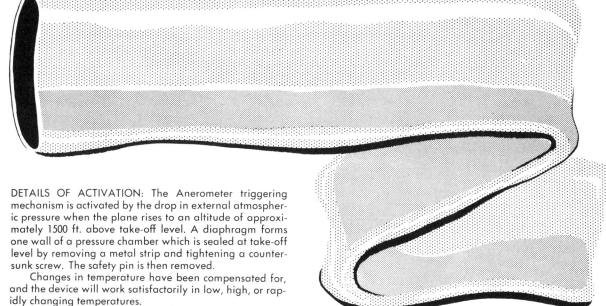

DETAILS OF ACTIVATION: The Anerometer triggering mechanism is activated by the drop in external atmospheric pressure when the plane rises to an altitude of approximately 1500 ft. above take-off level. A diaphragm forms one wall of a pressure chamber which is sealed at take-off level by removing a metal strip and tightening a countersunk screw. The safety pin is then removed.

Changes in temperature have been compensated for, and the device will work satisfactorily in low, high, or rapidly changing temperatures.

OVER →

SUGGESTED INSTALLATIONS: The assembled Anerometer is constructed in a size and shape for ready concealment in innumerable locations on enemy aircraft. Best examples of these are the weight-lightening holes in the wall of the wheel wells, accessible when the wheels are down. These holes open directly under the wing fuel tanks and cannon ammo. drums, insuring total destruction. The weapon can also be placed in the tail assembly where the lifting bar is inserted.

Installed between the engines of a larger ship, it will tear off the wing and outer engine. In any plane with wing-mounted engines, the structure of the wing can be shattered close to the fuselage and the weight of the engine will tear it off. Chest-heavy German craft are particularly vulnerable in the front where the personnel is concentrated, or in the long narrow fuselage and tail structure which can be blown away.

Many of these installations are in apertures not usually checked in pre-flight inspections. A booklet of detailed installation instructions is being prepared and will be included in shipments of the weapons.

RESTRICTED

DESCRIPTION: The Beano is a small, fragmentation grenade operated by an impact fuse. Its size and weight has been designed to approximate that of an American baseball. It has two arming mechanisms: (1) an arming pin that must be manually removed; and (2) an in-flight arming system that is activated only after the Beano has been thrown.

PURPOSE: The Beano is a lethal fragmentation grenade designed to explode on contact with a target. Conventional US and British hand grenades explode only after a set time delay. Too frequently the grenades bounce off the target and explode harmlessly on the ground. The Beano explodes only when it has made contact. With its dual arming systems, the pin on the grenade may be pulled and the grenade held safely until the target is within range. A minimum throw of 25' is then necessary to ensure that the in-flight arming system has been activated so that it will explode on contact. The killing radius of the Beano is 10' from the impact point.

size: . . . . 9 1-2" in circumference
weight . . . . 11 oz.

Very good use of the Beano can be made for attacks on stationary aircraft, moving vehicles, and other targets that require explosion on contact for optimum destruction.

EXPLOSIVE COAL*

DESCRIPTION: Explosive Coal looks like an ordinary, large piece of coal. It is actually a hollow shell with a reinforced interior that can be packed with explosives. Two small openings in the outer shell allow a means by which the coal can be ignited. The explosive charge must be ordered separately.

PURPOSE: Explosive Coal is a method of camouflaging a powerful demolition charge. The coal is camouflaged by painting it to match the color of the coal being used by the enemy. After camouflaging and packing with explosives, the coal is secretly dropped into the coal bin at the railroad yard or shipyard. While the enemy guards his installations carefully, he frequently does not guard his coal dumps. The explosive coal can be casually tossed or dropped into the coal dump from a motorcar, bicycle, or while walking in the area. When it is subsequently burned, the fire ignites the charge and results in a destructive explosion. The camouflage kit must also be ordered separately.

weight . . . . approximately 3 lbs.

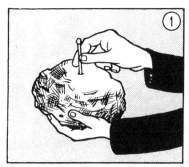

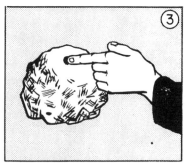

ISSUED BY: OSS

COAL CAMOUFLAGE KIT*

DESCRIPTION: The Coal Camouflage Kit is issued in a small, olive-drab colored, metal box. It can easily be carried in a jacket pocket. The kit contains:
  a) vial of paint thinner
  b) tubes of paint pigment
  c) contour putty plugs
  d) spatula
  e) paint brushes of varying sizes
  g) pen knife with 2" blade
  h) small cloth
  i) illustrated instruction sheet (available in various languages)

PURPOSE: The Coal Camouflage Kit contains everything necessary to camouflage a lump of explosive coal. Using the tools and paints provided in the kit, explosive coal can be camouflaged to match the color of the coal being burned in enemy boilers. The camouflaged, explosive coal is dropped in the enemy coal bin to be burned as fuel for his locomotive engine.

length . . . . 3 1-8"
width . . . . 6"
height . . . . 1 1-8"

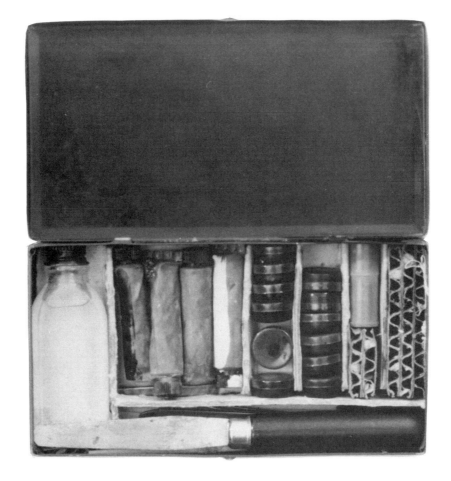

SSTR-1 SUITCASE RADIO*

DESCRIPTION: The SSTR-1 is a small, complete shortwave radio transmitter and receiver. The unit is transportable and can be carried in a back pack or suitcase. It weighs from 20 to 44 lbs. depending on the type of carrier and power supply. A parts kit is normally included and contains various spares.

PURPOSE: The SSTR-1 is a powerful, small, and highly portable radio station intended for use by intelligence and special forces personnel. It is well suited for a variety of clandestine communication tasks and can be powered by a variety of energy sources. The SSTR-1 has an operational range of 1000 miles.

The SSTR-1 is comprised of four basic components:
- a) Transmitter
- b) Receiver
- c) Power supply
- d) Spare parts kit

The SSTR-1 is available in either a civilian-style suitcase, or a green fiber transportation case.

transmitter . . . . 4″ wide, 3″ deep, 9 1-2″ long
receiver . . . . 4″ wide, 3″ deep, 9 1-2″ long
power supply . . . . 6″ wide, 3 1-2″ deep, 9 1-2″ long
                      (dimensions vary with unit)
weight . . . . 20–44 lbs.
          depending on power supply and style of case

transmitter coverage . . . . . 3.0 to 14.0 Mc in three bands
power output . . . . 8–15 watts, 1 tube
transmitter . . . . Radiotelegraph type
receiver coverage . . . . 2.7 to 17 Mc in two bands
receiver . . . . superheterodyne-type receiving voice, tone, and cw, 5 tubes
power requirements . . . . 110 or 220v.AC (25 to 60 cycle); 6 v.DC; hand generator, wood-burning thermocouples
range . . . . long range, 300–1000 miles

ISSUED BY: OSS

SSR-5 MINIATURE RADIO*

DESCRIPTION: The SSR-5 is a powerful, portable radio receiver. It is packaged in a small, black metal case with a removable lid. The large vernier tuning control can be easily operated by an operator wearing gloves. The set has built-in connectors to accept external ground and aerial wires. The reception of the set is limited only by the frequency of operation, time of year, hour of operation, and selection of an adequate ground and aerial.

PURPOSE: The SSR-5 is designed to allow personnel operating behind enemy lines to receive coded radio messages in either voice or C.W. The SSR-5 does not have a built-in speaker, and requires the use of external earphones. Because of its small size, the SSR-5 can be effectively concealed in a suitcase or within a dwelling.

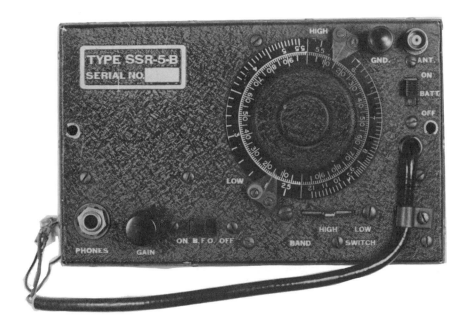

length . . . . 7 1-2"	coverage . . . . 2.5 to 12 Mhz. in two bands
height . . . . 3 1-2"	operation . . . . superheterodyne, 6 tubes
width . . . . 4 5-8"	power . . . . battery, 1.5v. A+
weight . . . . 2 3-4 lbs.	135v. B+
	6v. C−

ISSUED BY: OSS

AN/PRC-1 SUITCASE RADIO*

DESCRIPTION: Radio Set AN/PRC-1 is a portable radio station intended for shortwave communication over medium distances from variable points.

The set is comprised of a radiotelegraph transmitter, a radio receiver, and a power supply common to both. All three are constructed in one unit which mounts in a civilian-style carrying case.

PURPOSE: The AN/PRC-1 is a completely portable radio receiving and transmitting set intended for use by intelligence and special forces personnel. The transmitter, receiver, and rectifier unit are concealed in a civilian-style suitcase. The suitcase radio may be safely carried in public without arousing suspicion of its contents.

frequency range . . . . 2.0 to 12.0 Mc in two bands
power output . . . . 30 watts
transmitter . . . . radiotelegraph type
receiver . . . . receiving voice, tone, and cw.
power requirements . . . . 115/150/200/220/250-v.
(50 or 60 cycle)
range . . . . Medium range, 100–250 miles

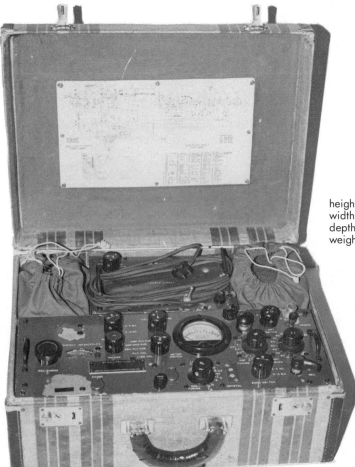

height . . . . 18″
width . . . . 13 1-4″
depth . . . . 7 1-4″
weight . . . . 32 lbs.

ISSUED BY: U.S. Army, Military Intelligence

RESTRICTED

DESCRIPTION: Radio Set AN/PRC-5 is a portable radio station intended for shortwave communication over medium distances from variable points.

The set is comprised of a radiotelegraph transmitter, a radio receiver, and a power supply common to both. All three are constructed in one unit which mounts in a luggage-style carrying case.

PURPOSE: The AN/PRC-5 is a completely portable radio receiving and transmitting set intended for use by intelligence and special forces personnel. The transmitter, receiver, and rectifier unit are concealed in a luggage-style suitcase. The AN/PRC-5 can be safely carried in public places without alerting onlookers to the contents of the suitcase.

transmitter coverage . . . . . 4.0 to 16.0 Mc in four bands
power output . . . . 10–16 watts
transmitter . . . . radiotelegraph type
receiver . . . . superheterodyne-type receiving voice, tone, and cw.
power requirements . . . . . . 110 or 220v. (50 or 60 cycle)
range . . . . medium range, 100–250 miles

height . . . . 11″
width . . . . 10″
depth . . . . 4 1-8″
weight . . . . 25 lbs.

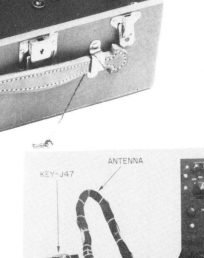

ISSUED BY: U.S. Army, Military Intelligence

RESTRICTED

SCR-504 DIRECTION-FINDING RADIO*

DESCRIPTION: Radio Set SCR-504 is a portable radio direction-finder (d/f) concealed within a pigskin suitcase. The radio receiver, BC-792-A, is an 8-tube superheterodyne covering a frequency range of from 100 kc to 65 mc. in eight bands. A miniature, hearing-aid size earpiece, jack and volume control are hidden beneath the carrying handle. A sensing rod antenna collapses into the top of the case.

PURPOSE: The SCR-504 is designed to identify the direction of enemy radio transmissions. The camouflaged appearance of the SCR-504 allows this direction-finding operation to be conducted openly without revealing its true purpose.

The radio's operation is not entirely unlike a normal portable radio at home. By turning it from side to side you identify the direction that gives the best results. With the SCR-504, however, this direction may also point to the location of the enemy transmitter.

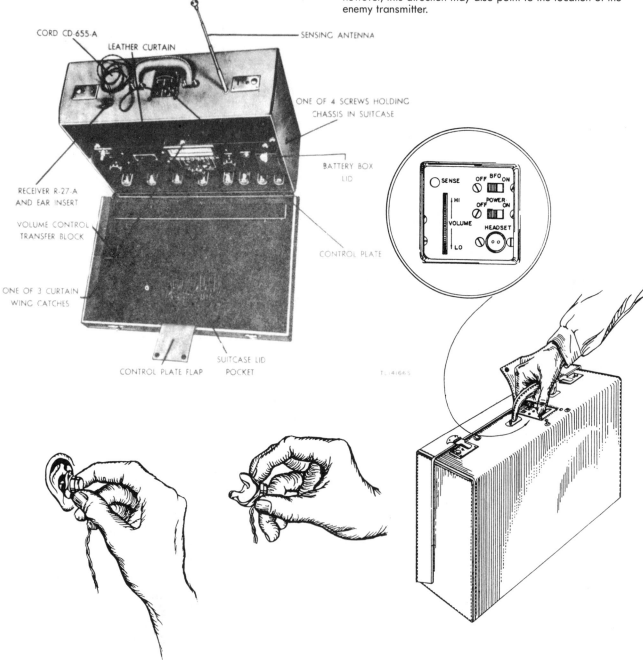

CORD CD-655-A

LEATHER CURTAIN

SENSING ANTENNA

ONE OF 4 SCREWS HOLDING CHASSIS IN SUITCASE

RECEIVER R-27-A AND EAR INSERT

BATTERY BOX LID

VOLUME CONTROL TRANSFER BLOCK

ONE OF 3 CURTAIN WING CATCHES

CONTROL PLATE

CONTROL PLATE FLAP

SUITCASE LID POCKET

SENSE OFF BFO ON

HI POWER OFF ON

VOLUME HEADSET

LO

TL-41665

ISSUED BY: U.S. Army, Military Intelligence

size . . . . 15 1-8" × 21 5-8" × 6 7-8"
weight . . . . 25.6 lbs.

TYPE B, MARK II SUITCASE RADIO*

DESCRIPTION: The Type B, Mark II Suitcase Radio is a powerful portable radio station. It may be ordered in a variety of concealments, including: (1) a civilian suitcase of a type consistent with luggage used within the target country; (2) a standard prewar portable phonograph case; and (3) an all metal, protective packing case (2 cases) for parachute drops.

PURPOSE: The Type B, Mark II is a powerful, compact, portable radio station designed for the transmission and reception of CW (coded) messages over long distances. The extremely sensitive receiver is selective and effective in pulling in weak signals. The powerful transmitter and versatile power supply allow for communication with a base station over distances in excess of 500 miles.

With its issue suitcase concealment, the Type B, Mark II may be carried in public without arousing suspicion. It appears identical with other suitcases in general use.

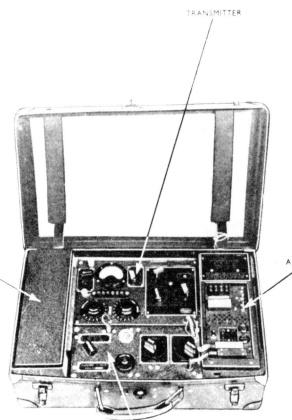

TRANSMITTER

POWER PACK A.C. OR BATTERY

BOX

RECEIVER

coverage . . . . 3.0 to 16.0 Mc/sec. on four plug-in tank coils for the transmitter, and 3.1 to 15.5 Mc/sec. in three wave bands for the receiver
power output . . . . average fundamental power, 20 watts
transmitter . . . . two tube transmitter, EL32 and 6L6G, crystal-controlled oscillator
receiver . . . . four tube, superheterodyne receiver designed primarily for CW (Morse code)
power supply . . . . 97 to 250 volts A.C. from house current, 6 volts from automobile accumulators

size . . 18 1-2" × 13 1-2" × 5 3-4" as shown in issue suitcase
weight . . . . 32 3-4 lbs.

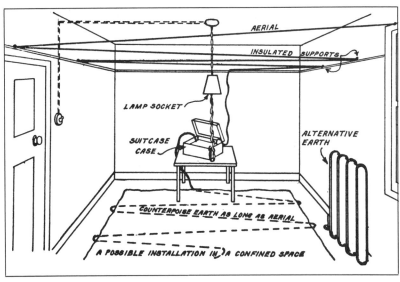

AERIAL

INSULATED SUPPORTS

LAMP SOCKET

SUITCASE CASE

ALTERNATIVE EARTH

COUNTERPOISE EARTH AS LONG AS AERIAL

A POSSIBLE INSTALLATION IN A CONFINED SPACE

ISSUED BY: SOE

TYPE A, MARK III SUITCASE RADIO*

DESCRIPTION: The Type A, Mark III Suitcase Radio is a powerful, portable, radio station. It may be ordered in two styles of cases: (1) a civilian suitcase; and, (2) an all metal, protective packing case for parachute drops.

PURPOSE: The Type A, Mark III is a powerful, compact, and portable radio station designed for the transmission and reception of CW (coded) messages. It is suitable for communication with a base station at distances up to 500 miles. The Type A, Mark III Suitcase Radio is the smallest portable radio set available. It may be safely carried in its small issue suitcase, or easily hidden in a house or apartment.

length . . . . 13"
height . . . . 8 1-4"
depth . . . . 4"
weight . . . . 13 lbs.

coverage . . . . 3.2 to 9.0 Mc in two bands: "blue band," 3.2 to 5.2 Mc, "red" band, 5 to 9 Mc
power output . . . . average power 5 watts
transmitter . . . . two tubes
receiver . . . . four tube, superheterodyne
power supply . . . . 100 to 250 volts A.C. from house current, 6 volts from automobile accumulators with optional vibrator supply

ISSUED BY: SOE

DESCRIPTION: Converter M-209 is a small compact, hand-operated, tape-printing, mechanical cipher machine. The converter is contained in a metal box, and is normally carried in a canvas case, suspended by a strap over the shoulder. The case has compartments for carrying the manual, pencils, extra tape, and message books. Inside the cover is a pair of tweezers, an oilcan, ink-pad can, and the roll of paper tape in use.

A military cipher system comprises a prearranged set of rules and aids chosen for encrypting messages sent from one unit (or agent) to another. A cipher system normally uses single letters to represent other single letters. Converter M-209 is a mechanical cipher device. It is designed to provide a high degree of security when operators are fully indoctrinated in the necessity for strict compliance with each rule for enciphering and when messages are prepared with a proper regard for security.

PURPOSE: When properly set and operated, the M-209 will encipher a plain-text message by substituting a letter for a letter, automatically printing the enciphered text on a paper tape in five-letter groups; or it will decipher a message that has been previously enciphered by another Converter M-209, printing the clear text on the tape.

Converter M-209 in use.

size . . . . 7 1-4" × 5 7-16" × 3 1-2"
weight . . . . 7 1-4 lb (including accessories)

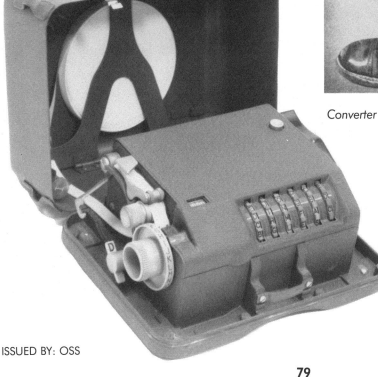

Components and accessories
1. *Canvas case*
2. *Converter M-209*
3. *Carrying strap*
4. *Hand strap*
5. *Screwdriver*
6. *Message clips*
7. *Tweezers*
8. *Oilcan*
9. *Ink pads*
10. *Ink-pad can*
11. *Paper tape*

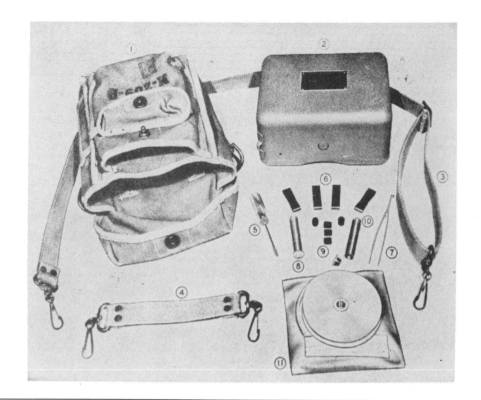

DESTRUCTION NOTICE

USE ANYTHING IMMEDIATELY AVAILABLE
FOR DESTRUCTION OF THIS EQUIPMENT

WHY   To prevent an enemy from using or salvaging this equipment for his benefit.

WHEN   When ordered by your commander, or when capture is imminent!

HOW   Smash—Use sledges, axes, handaxes, pickaxes, hammers, crowbars, heavy tools, heel of a boot, etc.

Cut—Use axes, handaxes, machetes, etc.

Burn—Use gasoline, kerosene, oil, flame throwers, incendiary grenades, etc.

Explosives—Use firearms, grenades, TNT, etc.

Disposal—Bury in slit trenches, fox holes, other holes. Throw in streams. Scatter.

WHAT   Smash—Everything; especially cipher rotors, wheels, gears, levers, etc.

Cut—canvas case, straps.

Burn—Cipher keys, technical manuals, paper tape, canvas case.

Bury or scatter—Any or all of the above pieces after breaking.

DESTROY EVERYTHING

M-94 CIPHER DEVICE*

DESCRIPTION: The M-94 Cipher Device is an aluminum cylinder that rotates along a central axis. The cylinder is constructed of 25 individual disks. Around the edge of each disk the 26 letters of the alphabet are listed in a random sequence. No two disks have the same arrangement of the letters in the alphabet. A knurled nut at the end of the cylinder allows the disks to be rotated freely or tightened to hold them in position. An external bar runs along the length of the cylinder to aid in the alignment of the disks and in reading the resulting cipher.

PURPOSE: The M-94 Cipher Device provides personnel in the field with a fast and efficient method of ciphering and deciphering messages. The M-94 Cipher Device does not offer the level of security that can be achieved with messages enciphered on the M-209 Cipher Machine. Use of the M-94 should be determined by, and conditional upon, the level of security required for the message to be transmitted.

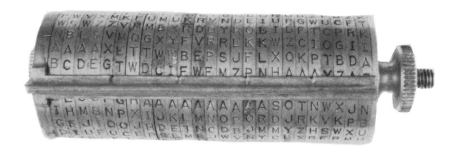

length . . . . 6"
diameter . . . . 2"

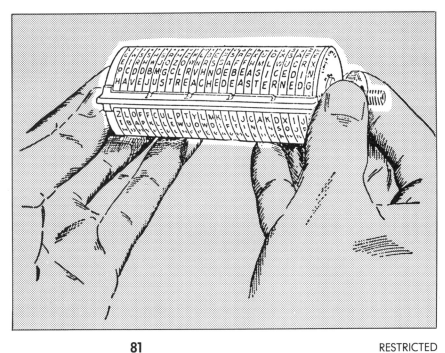

ONE-TIME PAD*

DESCRIPTION: The One-Time Pad is comprised of 10 key sheets and is issued with one silk grid. The keys are printed on a special paper that allows instant destruction by water or flame. The silk grid is the size of a small handkerchief and can not be creased. It may be rolled into a very small cylinder and hidden in any number of readily available items such as a fountain pen, or razor handle.

PURPOSE: The One-Time Pad system offers an extremely quick and easy system of enciphering and deciphering messages. The system requires little attention and generates few errors. Of greatest importance is that the cipher is mathematically unbreakable. Only the "home" station has a matching set of One-Time Pads and silk grids. Each key sheet of the One-Time Pad must be destroyed after being used only once! For security reasons, the One-Time Pad and silk grid should not be kept together.

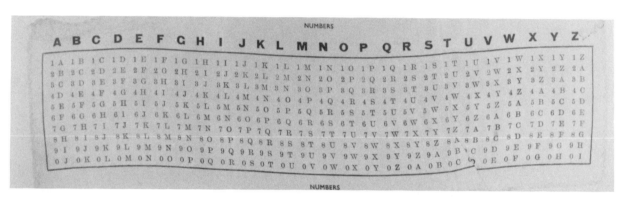

ISSUED BY: OSS

grid sheet . . . . 10 1-2" × 3 1-4"
key sheets . . . . 8" × 8"

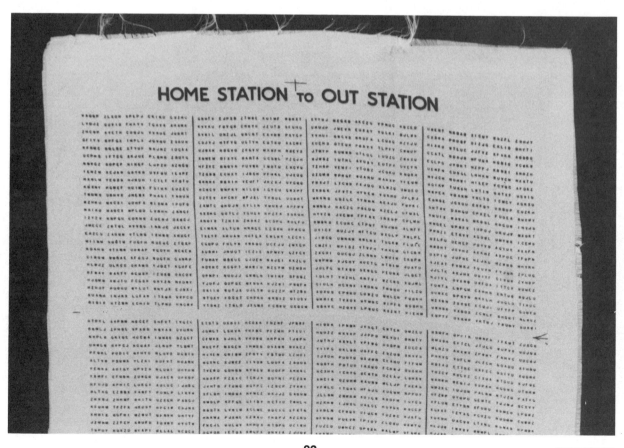

DESCRIPTION: Who, Me? is a soft metal tube with a screw cap on a projecting tip. When the cap is removed and the tube squeezed it squirts a liquid chemical of violent, repulsive, and lasting odor. Each tube is covered by a cardboard sleeve for protection of the operator.

PURPOSE: Who, Me? is a psychological harassing agent. It is to be squirted directly upon the body or clothing of a person a few feet away. The odor is that of occidental feces, which is extremely offensive to the orientals. Very good use of this agent can be made by native patriots in crowded markets and bazaars to create disturbances, attack morale of enemy guards, and to divert attention from other activities.

size . . . . 2 3-4" X 1-2" overall
weight . . . . 1-2 oz.
packed 5 to a waterproof envelope

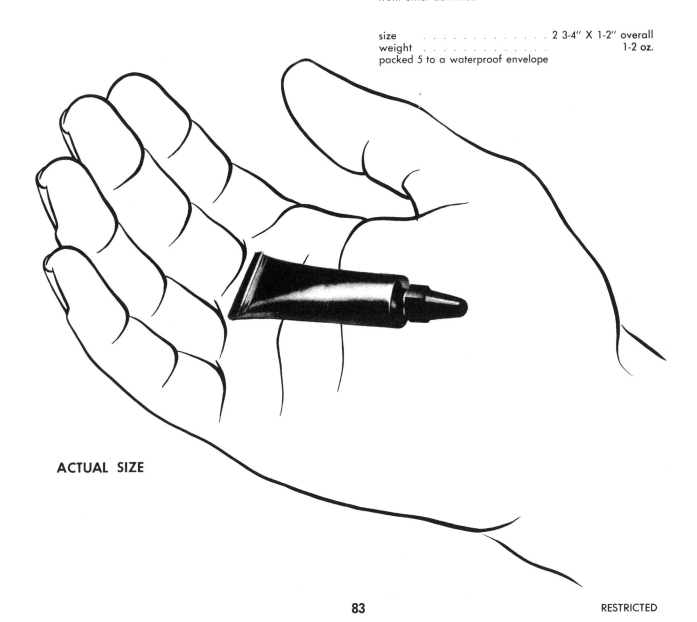

ACTUAL SIZE

DOG DRAG

DESCRIPTION: The Dog Drag is a small metal case containing a glass ampule which can be broken by a thumb screw. The ampule contains a persistant aromatic fluid which soaks on to the cloth wick of the drag. The whole device is trailed behind the operator by a heavy 6 foot string.

PURPOSE: The Dog Drag is to throw trained dogs off the scent of their quarry. Its technique requires careful study of the instructions and diagrams, and of the terrain. It can be particularly useful in disguising the operator's trail to a hidden storage point or other revisited spot.

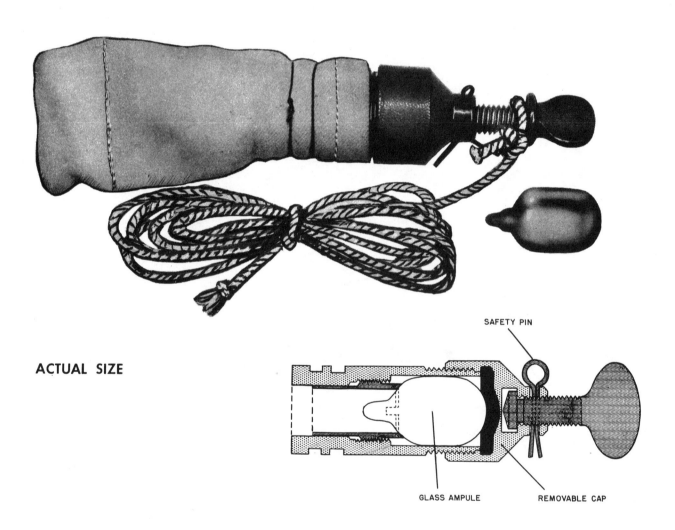

ACTUAL SIZE

SAFETY PIN

GLASS AMPULE   REMOVABLE CAP

size . . . . 6" X 1" Diam.
weight . . . . 4 1-2 oz.
packed 3 to a metal container (includes 3 ampules)
weight of container . . . . 1 lb. 2 oz.

FIREFLY (INCENDIARY EXPLOSIVE)

DESCRIPTION: The Firefly is constructed of three parts screwed together to form a small unit easily held in one hand. A safety pin at the small end prevents premature firing. The incendiary has a self-contained time delay. The usual delay is from 2 to 7 hours, depending upon the temperature of the gasoline in which it is immersed. Lower temperatures cause the longer delay.

PURPOSE: The Firefly is a small-sized explosive incendiary which can be easily palmed into the gasoline tanks of motor vehicles and gasoline storage containers, such as tanks, drums and cans. It causes a violent explosion,

blowing a large hole in the container and resulting in most cases in instantaneous fire. The explosive charge and igniting character accomplish complete vehicle demolition by the resulting fire. The incendiary has a built-in time delay device to allow the operator to leave the vicinity before the explosion.

The time delay is accomplished by two rubber washers which swell when immersed in gasoline. As they swell, they withdraw a plunger, permitting a firing pin to strike a percussion cap, firing a charge.

The operator merely withdraws the safety pin and slips the Firefly into the gasoline tank. He should check for rods or screens preventing the entry of the device into the tank.

It must be immersed in gasoline to become activated.

```
size . . . . . . . . . . . . . . . 3 7-16" x 1 3-8" diam.
weight . . . . . . . . . . . . . . . . . . .    3 oz.
packed 4 to a can
```

ACTUAL SIZE

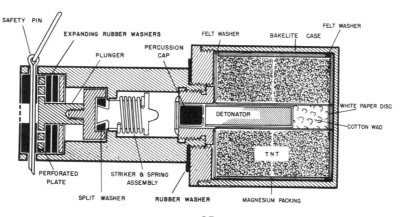

DESCRIPTION: Caccolube is a small thin-rubber sac (prophylactic sheath), containing a gritty chemical compound that damages and destroys any type of internal combustion engine. Its size is approximately 2 1-2" x 1 1-4" x 1". The extra length of the sheath is twisted and folded to retain the contents.

PURPOSE: To disable permanently the bearings, pistons and cylinder block of any internal combustion engine. This simple device can be easily concealed in the palm of one hand and slipped into the oil intake of any engine. After the engine heats up, the hot oil will deteriorate the rubber sac and free the compound into the lubricating system. When circulated through this system the compound fuses and welds the moving metal parts of the machinery.

Slipped into a truck, the Caccolube takes effect after the truck has been driven from 30 to 50 miles. It reacts so thoroughly on pistons, cylinder walls, and bearing journals that the vehicle is not only thrown out of service but the engine is destroyed beyond repair. Effective use is unlimited against engines operating on land, sea and air. A probe or stick will insure that the Caccolube is not hung up in the oil intake on rods or baffles. If necessary the sac can be opened and any liquid added to the compound. With approximately 4 parts of liquid to the amount of powder, a slurry can be mixed for pouring into the lubricating system. It will be distributed more quickly to the vital parts and will put the engine out of action a short time after warming up.

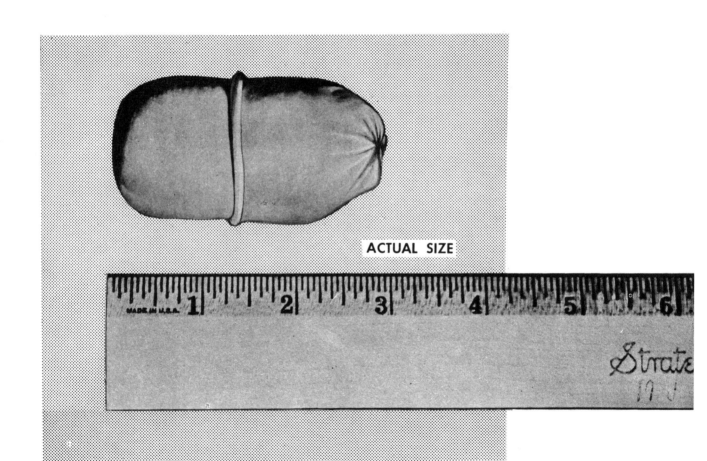

ACTUAL SIZE

size . . . . 2 1-2" x 1 1-4" x 1"
weight . . . . 2 oz.
packed in lots of 5 to a metal container

TIRE SPIKE*

DESCRIPTION: The 4″ diameter Tire Spike is made from heavy steel with four points alternately bent in a 45 degree angle from the horizontal.

PURPOSE: The Tire Spike is designed to puncture rubber tires on both vehicles and airplanes. With its nonreflective finish, the spikes are especially effective when scattered along enemy roads or on airfield runways. No matter how the Tire Spike is thrown or dropped, one of its four spikes will land in a vertical, upright position.

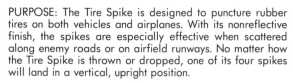

size . . . . 4″ diameter

ISSUED BY: OSS

SABOTEUR'S KNIFE*

DESCRIPTION: This special Saboteur's Knife features both a conventional lock-blade, and a special "hawk-bill" slashing blade. When closed, the knife, with its bakelite handles, appears to be only a common utility knife.

PURPOSE: The knife and its special blade is intended to give an agent ready access to a weapon designed to quickly disable motor vehicles. The leverage provided by the small hawk-bill blade allows the agent to cut vehicle tires using a carving motion to the sidewalls.

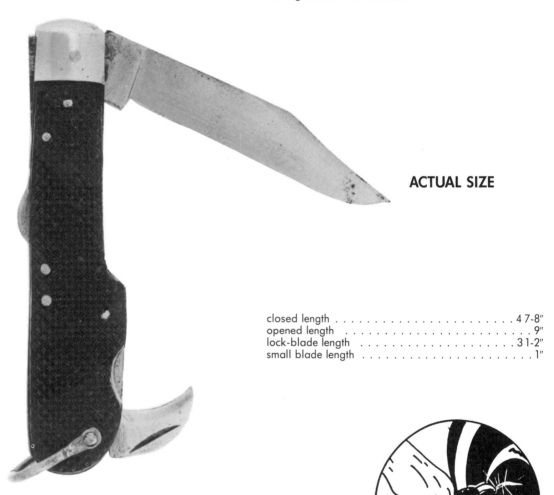

ACTUAL SIZE

```
closed length  . . . . . . . . . . . . . . . . . . . . . . 4 7-8"
opened length  . . . . . . . . . . . . . . . . . . . . . . 9"
lock-blade length  . . . . . . . . . . . . . . . . . . . . 3 1-2"
small blade length  . . . . . . . . . . . . . . . . . . . . 1"
```

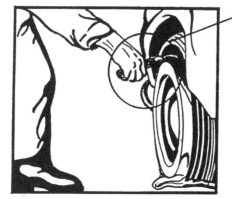

Tires that have been slashed on the sidewalls are not repairable!

ISSUED BY: SOE

FIRING DEVICE—PRESSURE TYPE A-3

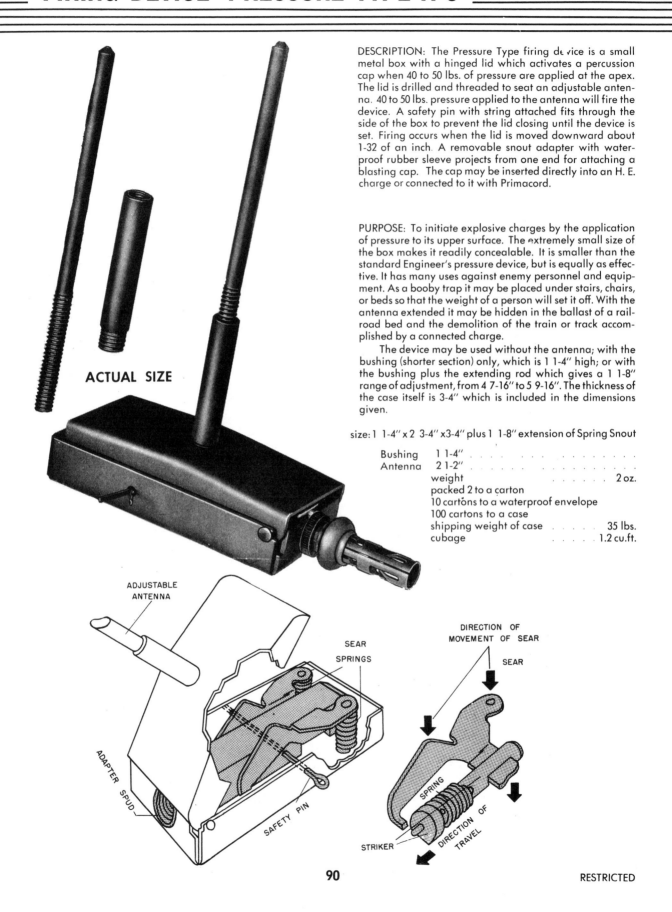

ACTUAL SIZE

DESCRIPTION: The Pressure Type firing device is a small metal box with a hinged lid which activates a percussion cap when 40 to 50 lbs. of pressure are applied at the apex. The lid is drilled and threaded to seat an adjustable antenna. 40 to 50 lbs. pressure applied to the antenna will fire the device. A safety pin with string attached fits through the side of the box to prevent the lid closing until the device is set. Firing occurs when the lid is moved downward about 1-32 of an inch. A removable snout adapter with waterproof rubber sleeve projects from one end for attaching a blasting cap. The cap may be inserted directly into an H. E. charge or connected to it with Primacord.

PURPOSE: To initiate explosive charges by the application of pressure to its upper surface. The extremely small size of the box makes it readily concealable. It is smaller than the standard Engineer's pressure device, but is equally as effective. It has many uses against enemy personnel and equipment. As a booby trap it may be placed under stairs, chairs, or beds so that the weight of a person will set it off. With the antenna extended it may be hidden in the ballast of a railroad bed and the demolition of the train or track accomplished by a connected charge.

The device may be used without the antenna; with the bushing (shorter section) only, which is 1 1-4" high; or with the bushing plus the extending rod which gives a 1 1-8" range of adjustment, from 4 7-16" to 5 9-16". The thickness of the case itself is 3-4" which is included in the dimensions given.

size: 1 1-4" x 2 3-4" x3-4" plus 1 1-8" extension of Spring Snout

Bushing	1 1-4"	
Antenna	2 1-2"	
	weight	2 oz.
	packed 2 to a carton	
	10 cartons to a waterproof envelope	
	100 cartons to a case	
	shipping weight of case	35 lbs.
	cubage	1.2 cu.ft.

ADJUSTABLE ANTENNA

SEAR SPRINGS

DIRECTION OF MOVEMENT OF SEAR

SEAR

ADAPTER SPUD

SAFETY PIN

SPRING

DIRECTION OF TRAVEL

STRIKER

FIRING DEVICE—RELEASE TYPE A-2

DESCRIPTION: The Release Type Firing Device is a metal housing with a hinged lid. The housing and lid have extending lips that project and fit closely together so that the device may be inserted into narrow cracks or under objects. When the device is set, the removal of an already fixed pressure from its upper surface (minimum 1 lb. on the lip end, more on the body) will cause a firing pin to strike a percussion cap.

This cap is seated in the snout adapter. The snout adapter is removable for inspection of the device before setting, and is covered with a waterproofing rubber sleeve. It will hold a blasting cap, the other end of which can be inserted directly into the H. E. charge or connected with Primacord. A safety pin is inserted through holes in the housing, lid and firing pin for safe handling, and is easily removed when the device is set. The whole unit is smaller than, but equally effective as, the standard Engineers' device for this purpose.

PURPOSE: This device is designed for initiating a hidden explosive charge by some action directly and unwittingly made by the enemy personnel. It may be installed under any object that is likely to be moved by the enemy. It can instill fear and cause loss of morale, as well as accomplishing demolition of equipment and personnel. The device fits into door and window cracks, and can be hidden in or under furniture, automobiles, trucks or other equipment.

The Release Device is particularly useful in booby trapping an explosive charge that is set with other means of activation which may be discovered by the enemy. (See Illustration). In this way the charge will be activated upon attempted removal, preventing the enemy from gaining knowledge of demolition methods and equipment. The Release Device has unlimited uses to augment other activating devices if problems of installation are carefully studied.

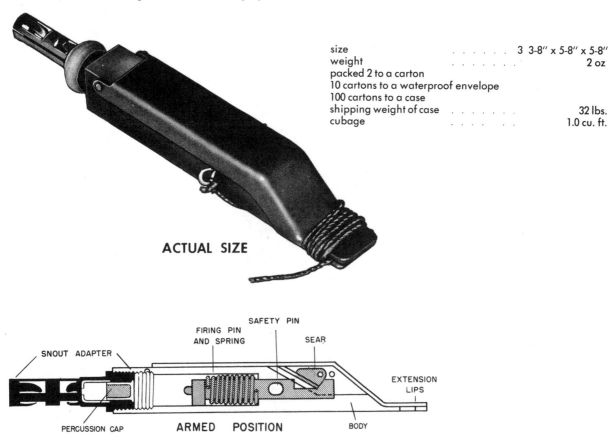

ACTUAL SIZE

size	. . . .	3 3-8″ x 5-8″ x 5-8″
weight	. . . .	2 oz
packed 2 to a carton		
10 cartons to a waterproof envelope		
100 cartons to a case		
shipping weight of case	. . . .	32 lbs.
cubage	. . . . . .	1.0 cu. ft.

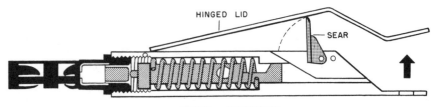

ARMED POSITION

FIRED POSITION

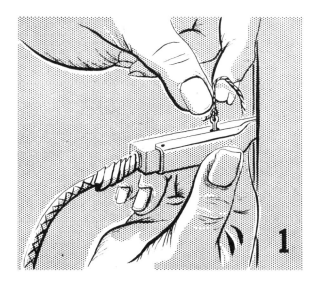

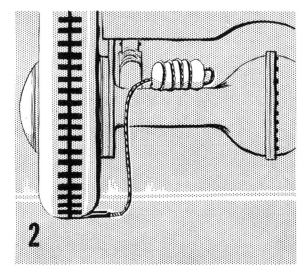

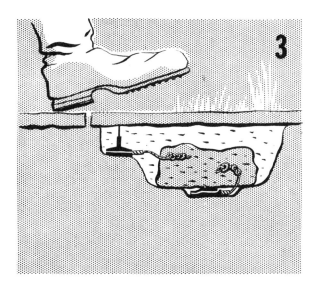

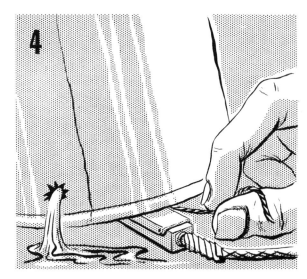

1. In a door jamb. Will fire when door is opened.

2. Under a vehicle wheel. Will fire when vehicle is moved.

3. Buried under a charge set with Pressure Device (or any delayed firing device). If charge is discovered by enemy, the Release Device will set off the charge as the discoverer tries to remove it. This is particularly useful in preventing the enemy from examining discovered demolition equipment and methods of use.

4. To make a crude improvised time delay. The water pail or tin can is punctured, allowing liquid to leak out slowly. When the lessening weight reaches 1 lb., the device will fire. The nearer the hinge of the lid the weight is placed, the heavier it must be to keep the device closed.

FIRING DEVICE—PULL TYPE A-2

DESCRIPTION: The Pull Type firing device is a cast metal housing containing a spring-loaded firing pin. The housing has a ring at one end for attaching a trip wire which will fire the device at a pull of from 3 to 6 lbs. A removable snout adapter, with waterproof rubber sleeve, projects from the other end for holding a blasting cap. This detonator can be inserted directly into an H. E. charge or connected to it with Primacord. There are two safety pins inserted through the housing and firing mechanism to insure safe handling. One of the safety pins has a 6" length of stout cord fastened to it. A 12" length of heavy cord is also threaded through an anchoring lug on the housing for securing the device in place.

PURPOSE: To activate an explosive charge by an unwitting action of the enemy. A pull on the trip wire of from 3 to 6 lbs. will fire the device. The unit may be concealed in the expected path of the enemy or in buildings, doorways, furniture, desk drawers or other places of likely activation. Its small size makes it easy to conceal. It is smaller than the standard Engineers' Pull Type device, but equally as effective.

size . . . . 3 1-4" long X 1-2" diameter
4 3-8" long including snout
weight . . . . 1 oz.
packed 2 to a carton
10 cartons to a waterproof envelope
10 envelopes (200 Devices) to a case
shipping weight of case . . . . 20 lbs.
cubage . . . . 1.0 cu. ft.

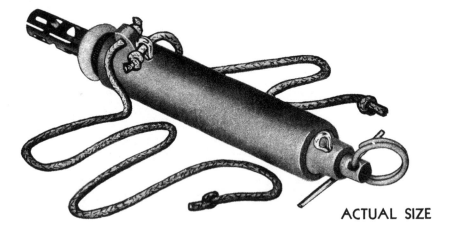

ACTUAL SIZE

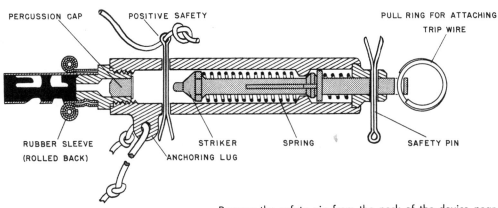

PERCUSSION CAP   POSITIVE SAFETY   PULL RING FOR ATTACHING TRIP WIRE

RUBBER SLEEVE (ROLLED BACK)   STRIKER   SPRING   SAFETY PIN

ANCHORING LUG

The two safety pins insure safety to the operator while installing the device. The charge can be placed and the firing device anchored securely. Connect the charge to the device with Primacord and a detonator in the spring snout adapter. Fasten the trip wire at its neutral anchorage first. Then attach it to the pull ring, drawing the wire only taut enough to remove the slack.

Remove the safety pin from the neck of the device near the pull ring. If the wire is too taut the firing pin will move forward but be blocked by the second safety pin near the snout adapter. In that case the second safety pin will be extremely difficult to remove due to the pressure on it from the firing pin. In normal operations without premature firing the second firing pin will slip easily from its hole and the installation is complete.

DESCRIPTION: Each Pencil is made of three sections: a soft copper tube, a brass tube, and a spring snout extension. The soft copper tube contains a glass ampule of corrosive liquid and a steel wire. The steel wire holds a spring-loaded firing pin in position. The brass tube contains the spring, firing pin, and a percussion cap. It has an inspection port for determining if premature firing has occurred. It also has a colored metal safety strip which must be removed when activating the Pencil. The spring snout will hold safety fuse or a blasting cap. For most operations a blasting cap will be used, inserted directly into the explosive charge.

PURPOSE: Time Delay Pencils are used to set off any explosive charge, Thermit Well or other device when an interval of time is desired between placing the charge and its explosion. The Pencils function silently and are a help in maintaining the security and safety of the operator installing the charge. They may be used in all kinds of attack upon innumerable targets, such as buildings, bridges, power lines, machinery and materiel.

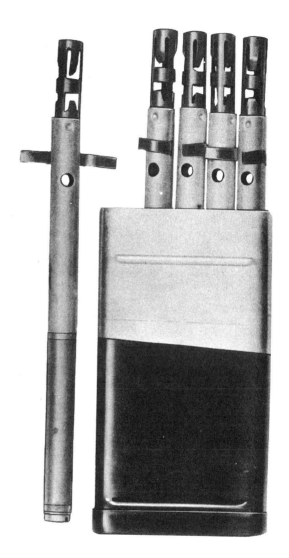

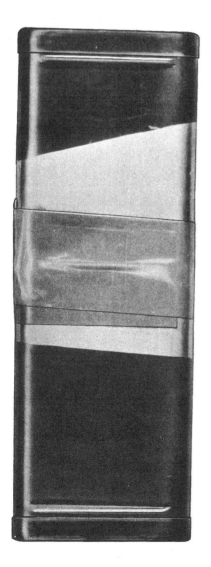

ACTUAL SIZE

The Pencils are issued in pocket-size metal boxes, each containing five Pencils of one delay period. (See Delay Chart). They are issued in complete sets: one box of each of the six various time periods. The color denoting the length of time delay is plainly marked on the metal safety strip on each Pencil. The adhesive tape sealing the box of five Pencils repeats the same color.

size of pencil	. . . .	5" X 1-4" diam.
weight of Pencil	. . . .	1 oz.
packed 5 to a can		
150 cans to a case		
shipping weight of case	. . . .	50 lbs.
cubage	. . . .	1.0 cu. ft.

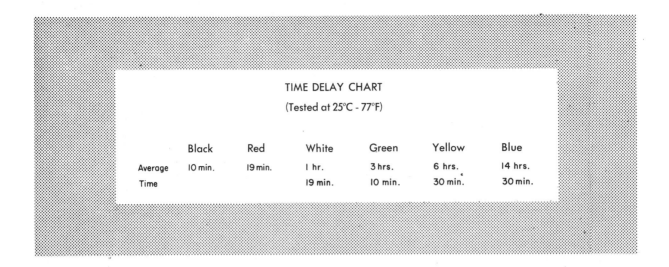

TIME DELAY CHART

(Tested at 25°C - 77°F)

	Black	Red	White	Green	Yellow	Blue
Average	10 min.	19 min.	1 hr.	3 hrs.	6 hrs.	14 hrs.
Time			19 min.	10 min.	30 min.	30 min.

Uses of the Time Pencils are unlimited and vary to suit each mission and tactical situation. To insure firing, at least two Pencils should be used for each installation. They may be used to ignite the short safety fuses on a Thermit Well. Blasting caps fixed in the spring snouts will initiate an H. E. charge, or Primacord leading to a charge. The safety fuse or blasting cap should be inserted firmly and fully into the spring snout. The most satisfactory results are obtained by placing the Pencils horizontally, but they will also function in any other position. One set of Pencils may activate several charges connected by Primacord.

Select the correct Pencils before going to the job. Make all possible preparations of charge beforehand.

At the Job:

1. Place the charge and install or connect the Pencils (blasting caps must be used with explosive charges).
2. Squeeze the soft copper tubes. Be sure inner glass vials are crushed.
3. Check the inspection ports to see that Pencils have not fired.
4. Remove the colored metal safety strips.

ACTUAL SIZE

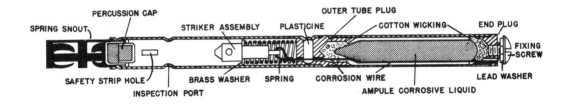

Temperature is important. In general, higher temperatures shorten the delay, and lower temperatures lengthen the delay. Therefore, short-delay Pencils are not often used in tropical heat, nor long-delay Pencils in extreme cold. More specific information is available.

DESCRIPTION: The AC Delay firing device gets its name from the action of the acetone and celluloid contents. The gray finished metal body is waterproof when tightly attached to the explosive weapon it will activate (See Limpet). A thumb screw, with removable safety pin, projects from one end of the body. This entire end is removable for inserting a glass ampule of colored liquid. When the ampule is crushed by the thumb screw the liquid eats through a celluloid disc, releasing a spring-loaded firing pin. The firing pin stabs a special detonator which sets off a booster charge. This insures detonation of the main H. E. charge in which the device is installed to activate.

PURPOSE: To set off an explosive charge after an approximate time delay period selected from a wide range (See chart). The metal body and fittings are waterproof and can be used in underwater installations of the Limpet and Pin-Up Girl. A variety of other uses can be planned by the operator to fit the tactical situation. The AC Delay with burster is primarily planned to set off large charges of insensitive high explosives.

The ampules of liquid are available in 6 different colors: red, orange, yellow, green, blue and violet. (The blue may fade to a colorless liquid.) Each color represents a different time delay. The following chart gives approximate or average delays. Particular attention should be paid to the effect of temperature. Present manufacture and current tests are aiming for greater accuracy. A new chart will be available soon.

The AC Delay is packed in a pocket-size tin box which holds one body (red ampule inserted); 5 extra ampules of assorted colors and varying delays; one combined detonator and booster unit; one time delay chart with brief instructions on the reverse side.

size	. . . . 5"- X 1" diam.
weight	. . . . 7 oz.
packed 1 to a metal container with 6 ampules and booster	
weight of container . , ...	10 oz.

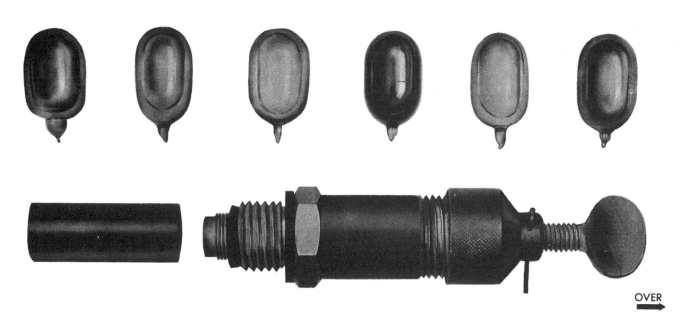

ACTUAL SIZE

OVER →

TEMP.	RED HOURS	ORANGE HOURS	YELLOW HOURS	GREEN HOURS	BLUE HOURS	VIOLET DAYS	TEMP.
40°F.	6½	9½	20	34	67	8½	5°C.
50°F.	5	8½	17	30	53	7	10°C.
60°F.	4½	7½	15	26	42	5½	15°C.
68°F.	4	7	14	22½	36	4½	20°C.
77°F.	3½	6½	12	20	30	3½	25°C.
88°F.	3	6	10	17½	25	2½	30°C.

NOTE: Subject to 15% deviation either way, except Red on which deviation may be 2 hours either way.

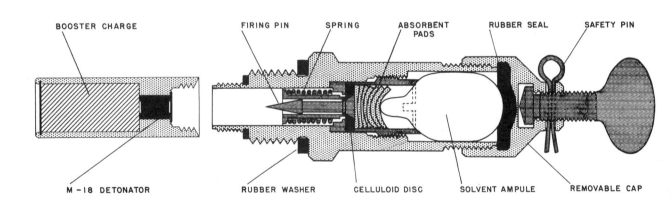

BOOSTER CHARGE · FIRING PIN · SPRING · ABSORBENT PADS · RUBBER SEAL · SAFETY PIN

M-18 DETONATOR · RUBBER WASHER · CELLULOID DISC · SOLVENT AMPULE · REMOVABLE CAP

DESCRIPTION: The Mark 3 Time Delay firing device is a small water-tight clock with a glass-covered luminous dial. Identification of the knobs and partial directions for use are concealed under O.D. masking tape on the back of the clock. The actual winding and setting screws are covered by removable threaded caps for water-proof protection. A combined screwdriver-key is included for these screws. The safety pin has a small knurled-edge disc for pulling and turning. It is not removed completely from the clock even when set for firing. A metal guard protecting the safety pin can be easily bent back or torn off. The safety pin cannot be pulled out if the device has fired. Operation can be tested and the device recocked and set by an experienced operator without removing the cover plates. The time delay range from setting until firing is from 15 minutes to 11 3-4 hours. The device is unsafe if the operator tries to set it for less than 15 minutes or more than 11 3-4 hours.

PURPOSE: To set off an explosive charge after a pre-set specific time delay. The clockwork will release the firing pin at any particular desired minute within a range of from 15 minutes to 11 3-4 hours. It is especially useful in a job demanding a specifically accurate delay which is unobtainable with chemical delay devices (Time Pencils and AC Delays).

The device is water-tight, will withstand water pressure at a depth of 20 feet, and is unaffected by high or low temperatures. Its running time is not affected by magnets. The sound of the simple watch mechanism is barely audible at close inspection. The unit is shipped cocked and unwound. It is threaded to receive either British or American attachments or, with a special adaptor and booster, for underwater use with the Limpet. Setting, winding, attaching to charge or booster connections can be done before arriving at the job. A start and stop wheel controls the actual running of the clock and may be turned on at the job.

size	2 3-4" X 2 1-2" X 1 1-2"
weight	11 oz.
packed 1 to a cardboard box	

ADHESIVE PASTE of great strength, functioning satisfactorily on wet, oily or dirty surfaces. Best results are obtained by applying evenly to both joining surfaces, but when impractical, coating of one surface gives a good bond. Care should be taken to rub the adhesive into the surfaces to be joined. Capable of long storage and effective over a wide range of temperatures. For best results the adhesive should be used at temperatures between freezing and 125°F.

Packaged in a screw cap lead tube.

size . . . . 5" X 1 1-2" diam.
weight . . . . 6 oz.

ADHESIVE TAPE is available in white or olive drab colors.

It is invaluable in making connections and improvised charges.

PLASTIC EXPLOSIVE (P.E.) AND PRIMACORD

Plastic explosive (P.E.) and Primacord can be put to many uses. The Primacord should be knotted and imbedded in the P.E., which is then folded over. The knots are essential for complete detonation, and should be centered in the charge.

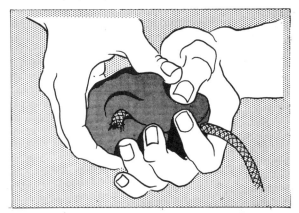

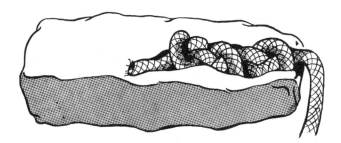

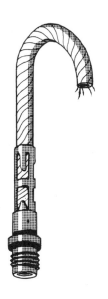

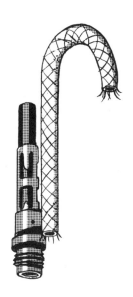

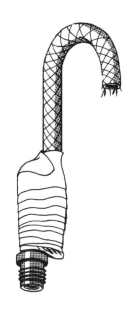

The percussion cap in the spring snout adapter will initiate safety fuse. To activate an explosive charge or Primacord leading to a charge, a detonator or blasting cap is required.
Fig. 1. Safety fuse seated properly in spring snout. Snout is provided with rubber sleeve which is rolled back for insert-ing the fuse, then unrolled to form a moisture-resistant pro-tection.
Fig. 2. Proper insertion of detonator into spring snout, with Primacord in position for taping.
Fig. 3. Primacord taped into position.

DETONATOR MAGAZINE—MAGNETS

THE DETONATOR MAGAZINE is a carrying container for 16 blasting caps. It is a tubular plastic barrel divided into 16 cylinders. The Magazine is loaded with 11 caps from one end and 5 from the other. The end covers can be rotated so that a hole in the cover aligns with the Cylinder for removing a cap.

size	. . . . .	2 3-4″ X 1 3-4″ diam.
weight	. . . . .	3 oz.
packed 100 to a case		
shipping weight of case	. . . . .	22 lbs.
cubage	. . . . .	.8 cu. ft.

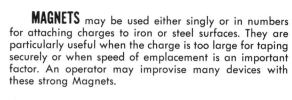

MAGNETS may be used either singly or in numbers for attaching charges to iron or steel surfaces. They are particularly useful when the charge is too large for taping securely or when speed of emplacement is an important factor. An operator may improvise many devices with these strong Magnets.

size	. . . .	2 1-4″ X 2″ X 1″
packed 100 to a case		
shipping weight of case	. . . .	55 lbs.
cubage	. . . . . .	.5 cu. ft.

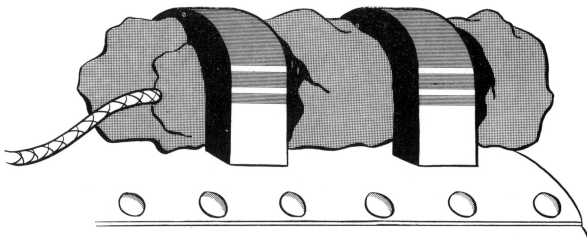

MATCH BOX (CAMERA)

DESCRIPTION: The Matchbox is a small black metal camera that resembles an ordinary penny match box in shape and size. Its dimensions are 2 3-8" X 1 1-2" X 7-8". The wide-angle lens is on one side edge, and the simple operating button is at one end. The lens has two openings, F.5 and F.16, easily adjusted by a small pin. There are two shutter speeds: instantaneous and bulb exposure. The fixed focus is from 4 1-2 ft. to infinity. The camera holds 2 ft., or 34 exposures, of any type of 16 mm. film. The image produced on the negative is 14 mm. square. It must be loaded and unloaded in the dark.

ACTUAL SIZE

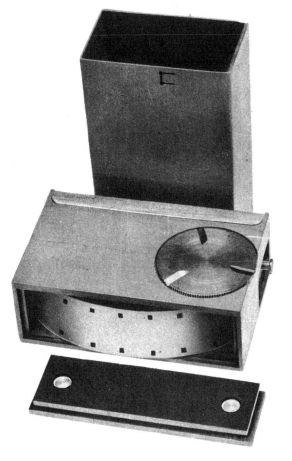

PURPOSE: Matchbox is an extremely small, accurate camera for general or documentary photography. It can be easily concealed and operated in one hand. There are innumerable means of camouflage or concealment. The camera can be requisitioned with labels like a Swedish or Japanese matchbox, or it can be requested plain for camouflage by the operator.

The camera is issued with 100 ft. of Plus X and 100 ft. of Super XX unperforated film. Any type of perforated or unperforated 16 mm. film will roll on the positive take-up spool. A tripod for documentary use is available on requisition. A compact developing kit is in preparation and will be ready in the near future.

size . . . . 2 3-8" X 1 1-2" X 7-8"
weight . . . . 4 oz.

OVER →

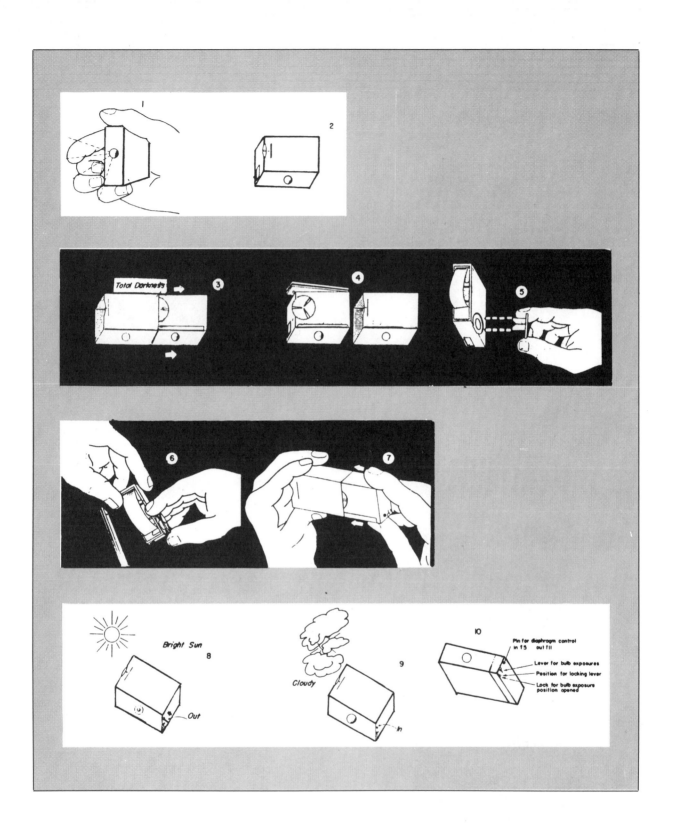

MINOX MINIATURE CAMERA*

DESCRIPTION: The Minox is a miniature stainless steel camera small enough to be concealed within the palm of the hand. Its dimensions are 3 1-8" × 1 1-16" × 19-32". A precision f3.5 lens is located on the side adjacent to the viewfinder window. The shutter-speed adjustment, shutter-release button, focus adjustment, and film-exposure counter are located on the top of the camera. The Minox is automatically in focus for all objects from 12' to infinity, and may be manually focused as close as 8". The shutter speed may be set from 1-2 second to 1-1000th of a second. The Minox holds 50 exposures of a 9 1-2 mm film. It may be loaded and unloaded in daylight.

PURPOSE: The Minox is an ultraminiature, precision camera with numerous applications in clandestine photography. It is ideally suited for photographing documents, but it may be also used for general photography. Its small size makes it easy to conceal and operate with one hand. When developed, the 8 1-2 mm × 11 mm Minox negatives will produce satisfactory prints up to 9" × 12".

ACTUAL SIZE

overall dimensions . . . . . . (including focal and exposure
    controls) 3 1-8" × 1 1-16" × 19-32"
weight . . . . 4 1-2 oz.
lens . . . . "Minostigmat" aperture f3.5
focal length . . . . 15 mm
size of negative . . . . . 5-16" × 7-16" (8 1-2 mm × 11 mm)
film . . . . . . unperforated film of 9.5 mm is used, factory
    loaded in a double-magazine and giving 50 exposures
    with one loading
Shutter . . 1-2 second to 1-1000th second with "B" and "T"
    settings for longer exposures
range of photos . . suitable for photographing all objects
    from 8" to infinity

ISSUED BY: OSS

A full range of accessories are available (must be ordered separately) including:
  (1) miniature daylight developing tank;
  (2) miniature enlarger;
  (3) miniature negative holder/viewer;
  (4) transformer;
  (5) special tripod head (not shown).

DESCRIPTION: "Gilhooley" is a contact paper printer in a metal container 11 1-2" X 15" X 2" in size. This container will fit in an ordinary briefcase. The container when opened serves as a tray for holding developing and fixing solutions.

All necessary accessories, extra supplies, paper and instruction booklet are furnished. The unit is supplied with a battery for the needed light source in making photo duplications, or it can be operated on commercial current if available.

PURPOSE: With the use of "Gilhooley" an operator can reproduce letters, documents, charts, maps, newspaper cuts, line drawings and half-tone illustrations. The maximum size of the reproduction is 9 1-2" X 14". Valuable information and graphic illustrations can be reproduced and distributed.

size . . . . 15" X 11 1-2" X 2"
weight . . . . 12 lbs.

PRESS X

DESCRIPTION: Press X is a miniature off-set printing press, 11" X 11" X 6" in size. It weighs approximately 13 lbs. complete. It is shipped in a plain suitcase container with instruction booklet, red and black ink, paper, plastic plates, and accessories. It uses any thickness of paper from tissue to cardboard. Sheet size can be any dimensions up to 5 1-2" X 8 1-2".

PURPOSE: For speedy reproduction of writing, printing, or drawing in any quantities. Writing or drawing can be made directly upon the grease-sensitive plates and reproduced quickly. The plates can be re-used. Duplicate plates can be made from the original plate.

This press has particular use in the publishing of underground newspapers, bulletins, instructions, reports and charts. In the near future a special camera will be available for use in the process of reproducing photographs. It will then be possible also to make large size copies of photos and plates.

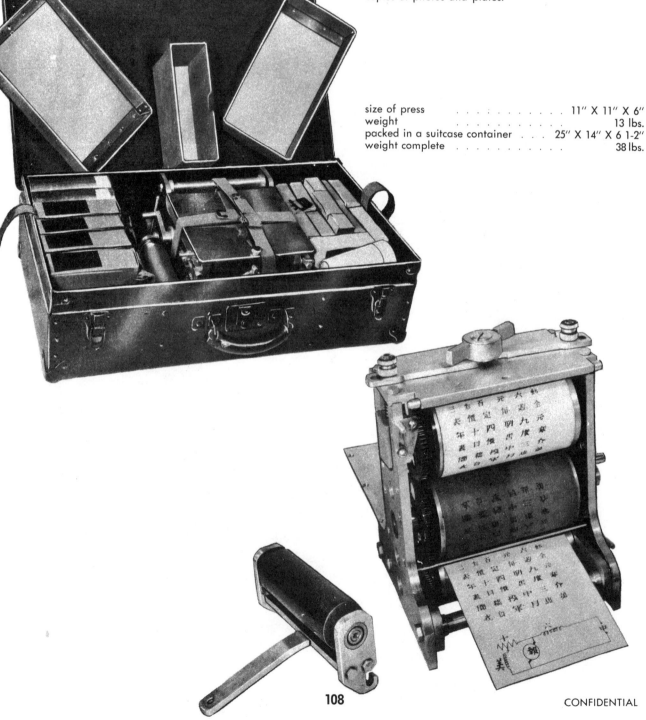

size of press	11" X 11" X 6"
weight	13 lbs.
packed in a suitcase container	25" X 14" X 6 1-2"
weight complete	38 lbs.

DESCRIPTION: The Medical Kit is a water-resistant canvas roll with separate pockets for 18 items and instruction booklet. The Kit is approximately 9" X 5" X 5", and weighs 2 1-2 lbs. The contained items vary to fit the needs of each theater of operations.

PURPOSE: To give each operator the necessary supplies for self-administered medical aid. The primary aim of the Kit is to help the operator prevent diseases and infections which may interfere with his efficiency. It also enables him to relieve pain, to combat bacteriological infections, and to dress wounds.

Standard individual items are replaceable from stores in local bases for each theater. Special medicines or supplies can be requisitioned in place of some of the standard items in the Kit.

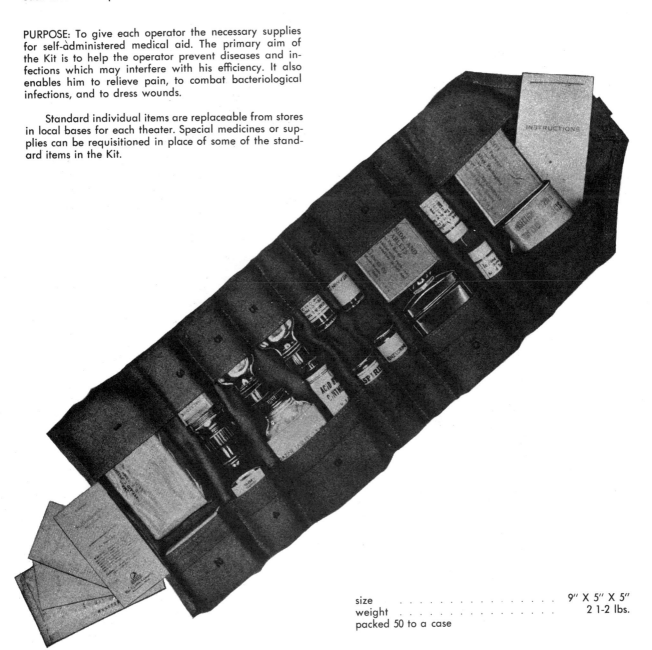

size . . . . 9" X 5" X 5"
weight . . . . 2 1-2 lbs.
packed 50 to a case

LOCKPICK KNIFE*

DESCRIPTION: The Lockpick Knife appears to be a common penknife. Inside, however, are five lockpicking tools and a standard 1 1-2" pen-blade. The knife is issued in a brown soft leather pouch.

PURPOSE: The lockpicking knife is designed to provide an operator with a small, easily concealable assortment of lockpicking tools. To effect a surreptitious entry, the operator would need only these lockpick tools, and a readily improvised torsion wrench.

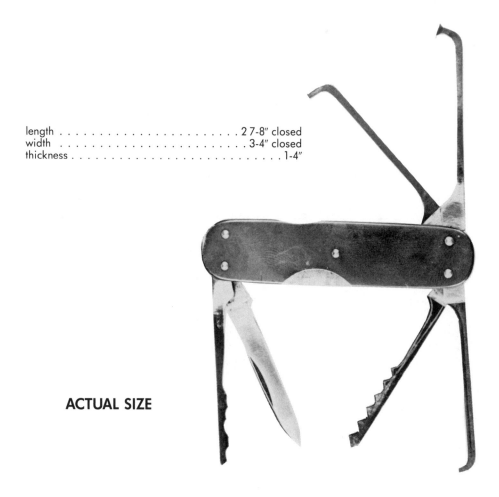

length . . . . 2 7-8" closed
width . . . . 3-4" closed
thickness . . . . 1-4"

ACTUAL SIZE

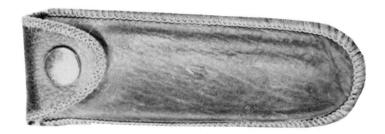

ISSUED BY: OSS

RESTRICTED

DESCRIPTION: The Escape Knife is a small, compact knife with the following features:
  a) built in wirecutter;
  b) screwdriver tip;
  c) conventional folding blade;
  d) three saw blades;
  e) pry-bar, or lockbreaker, blade.

PURPOSE: The Escape Knife is designed to provide personnel with a small, easily concealed weapon containing tools useful for escape and evasion.

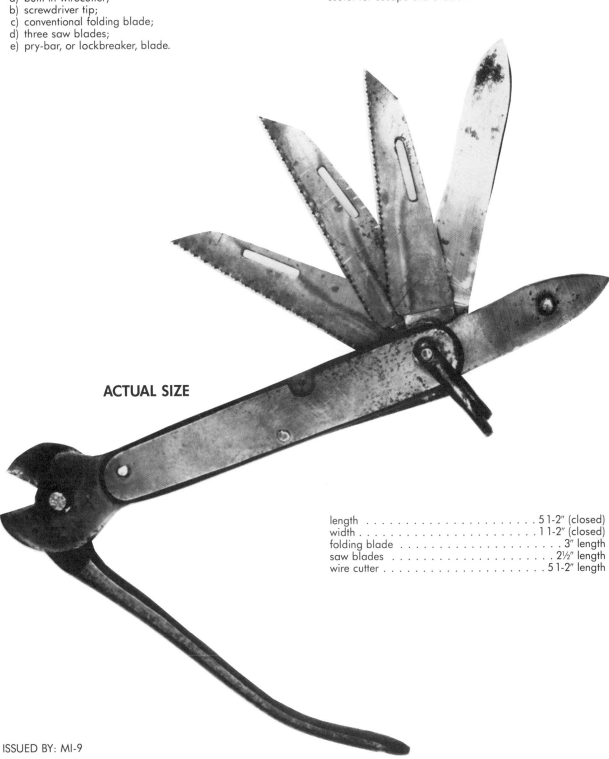

ACTUAL SIZE

length	5 1-2" (closed)
width	1 1-2" (closed)
folding blade	3" length
saw blades	2½" length
wire cutter	5 1-2" length

ISSUED BY: MI-9

RESTRICTED

ESCAPE KIT*

DESCRIPTION: The Escape Kit is made of rubberized linen. The kit is waterproof and contains:
a) one small compass;
b) one silk map;
c) one small saw blade;
d) three document-size photographs of the bearer in civilian clothes.

ISSUED BY: MIS-X

PURPOSE: The Escape Kit is small, flat, and can be readily concealed in personal equipment or clothing. The silk map is noiseless when being folded and unfolded. The compass has been waterproofed so that it may be utilized in any weather conditions. Personnel being issued this kit should immediately have three document-size photographs prepared while wearing civilian clothes. These photographs are to be carried in the Escape Kit and used in the preparation of forged escape documents.

escape kit . . . . 5″ × 5″
compass . . . . 9-16″ diameter
escape saw . . . . 4″ × 1-2″
photographs . . . . 1 3-4″ × 1 1-2″
escape map . . . . varying sizes
depending on area of coverage

DESCRIPTION: The button is identical in outward appearance to a standard issue military button. Contained inside, however, is a special waterproofed pivot-compass.

PURPOSE: The button compass is designed to be worn as a standard component of uniform accoutrement. When sewn on a uniform, it has the same appearance and functionality of the issue military service button. In the event of capture, or an emergency, the button can be quickly transformed into an effective escape and evasion compass. The button and concealed compass are designed to go undetected during a routine search and examination.

Buttons and compasses are produced with four types of concealments:
- (1) right-hand threads;
- (2) left-hand threads;
- (3) pressure fit;
- (4) hinged.

size . . . available in both coat-size and cuff-size buttons
weight . . . consistent with standard military issue buttons
style . . . . . . button compasses are available for various allied uniforms and services

ISSUED BY: MIS-X

SLEEPING BEAUTY*

DESCRIPTION: The Sleeping Beauty motorized submersible canoe is a one-man miniature submarine. The hull is an original design that can be used as a surface craft or can be submerged to a depth of 50'. The craft is 12'8" with a 27" beam, and weighs 600 lbs. There is ample room in the cockpit for the pilot, and a watertight cockpit cover fitted with a zip fastener makes it possible, when running on the surface, to render the craft entirely dry and splash proof.

On the surface, the Sleeping Beauty can be paddled, sailed, or electrically self-propelled. The Sleeping Beauty is equipped with a 24 volt 0.4 h.p. engine driven by four 6 volt batteries. The craft can cover, on the surface, a distance of 12 miles at a full speed of 4.5 knots, or 40 miles at a cruising speed of 3.0 knots. When submerged, the craft can achieve a speed in excess of 2 knots.

PURPOSE: The Sleeping Beauty is designed for attacks on enemy shipping in harbors, as well as the transportation of its pilot to an enemy shore. In both instances, the pilot (operator) wears a waterproof, cold-resisting, underwater rubber swim-suit, and breathes through a self-contained rebreathing apparatus.

size . . . . 12'8" length, 27" beam
power . . . . . . a. 24 volt 0.4 h.p. motor powered by four, 6 volt—89 ampere batteries
b. for sailing, a 6' mast is carried in two parts, with a 36 sq. ft. parachute silk sail
c. lightweight paddles, built in four parts, are provided
weight . . . . 600 lbs
communications . . . . Type A, Mark III suitcase radio, and accessories, is available in a special watertight case
armament . . . . limpet charges

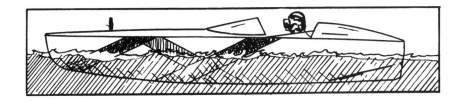

Cruising on the surface.

In the semi-submerged or attacking position.

For the attack on an enemy ship, the operator would pilot his craft just beneath the surface towards the enemy vessel. As the Sleeping Beauty makes contact with the target vessel, the craft is switched off and allowed to slowly sink. The operator swims away from the craft and places limpet charges on the hull of the target. The operator then swims back to his craft, and proceeds to a rendezvous with his rescue vessel. The limpet charges explode after a predetermined interval to allow for the safe withdrawal of the Sleeping Beauty.

To transport an operator to an enemy shore, the craft proceeds from its mother vessel while running just below the surface. When the enemy shore has been reached, the Sleeping Beauty is switched off and allowed to sink to the bottom in a shallow location. A phosphorescent buoy is attached to aid the operator in relocating his craft at a later time. The Operator swims to the shore and carries out his mission. Upon returning to the shore, he relocates his craft and proceeds submerged to his mother boat.

The operator is shown wearing a self-contained underwater rebreather. He is carrying a waterproof Type A, Mark 3 radio.

WELBIKE*

DESCRIPTION: The Welbike is a small, portable motorcycle powered by a 98-cc, two cycle engine. Its design allows it to be folded to reduce its size even further for transport.

PURPOSE: The Welbike is designed to fit (folded) within a standard parachute container. It is intended to provide special forces personnel with transportation to rapidly depart a landing area, or drop zone with their equipment.

height	15"
length	51"
width	12"
weight	70 lbs
assembly time	11 sec.
engine	98-cc Villiers, two cycle
range	90 mi.
top speed	30 MPH

ISSUED BY: SOE

DESCRIPTION: This canvas Jump Suit uses a mottled dark/green-brown-tan pattern to provide effective camouflage for parachute drops and air operations. A padded jump helmet and goggles provide protection on landing. Two full-length zippers allow a rapid exit from the suit upon landing. (A suit of identical design, but in white or tan, is available for parachuting into snow or desert sand.)

The parachute jump suit has special pockets for:

a) shroud knife (gravity);
b) folding shovel;
c) flashlight;
d) pistol;
e) fighting knife;
f) medical kit;
g) maps;
h) money (paper and gold);
i) L-tablet (lethal);
j) "spine" pad.

PURPOSE: The camouflage Jump Suit and padded helmet provide a safe and efficient method of parachuting an agent and his equipment into occupied territories. The full-length zippers allow the agent to "walk out" of the suit quickly upon landing. Adequate equipment is contained within the suit to sustain the agent in the event he is separated from his supplies or is not met by his reception committee upon landing.

size . . . . standard chest sizes

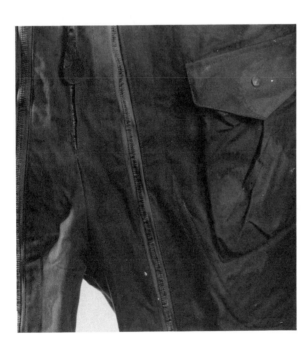

Civilian clothing may be easily and safely worn beneath the camouflage suit during the parachute jump.

ISSUED BY: OSS

Appendix

OSS SUPPLIES AT ALGIERS BASE, SPRING 1943

Supplies and Equipment for Base Staff

- Six months standard rations for 80 men
- Field equipment for 80 men
- Office equipment for a headquarters, a radio station, and a training school
- 12 trucks, eight cars, and three long-range, high-speed boats.

Supplies for a Guerrilla Force of 3000

Weapons with ammunition:

- 2000 Thompson sub-machine guns with one million rounds of ammunition
- 1000 .38 calibre pistols with 50,000 rounds
- 100 .45 calibre pistols with 5000 rounds
- 12 Reising sub-machine guns with 12,000 rounds
- 12 Garand rifles with 6000 rounds
- 40,000 hand grenades.

Explosives and sabotage equipment:

- 500 land mines
- 1000 pressure-release switches
- 1000 pull switches
- 1500 reels of friction tape
- Primacord (instantaneous fuse) and other stores for making up charges
- 200 three-cell flashlights with 1000 batteries

Survival kit:

- 2000 hunting knives
- 1100 jackknives
- 1500 standard portable compasses
- 3000 first aid kits and 500 special medical supply packs

Rations and clothing:

- 3000 K rations
- 3000 standard rations for three months, plus 500 special supplements
- 5000 sets of boots, underclothes, shirts, and slacks

Intelligence Gathering and Associated Items

Miniature cameras:

- 10 with accessories
- Darkroom equipment and supplies

Optical aids:

- 12 field glasses (six pair with 8x magnification)
- Four telescopes

Mapmaking equipment:

- 100 portable sets
- 200 sets map-reading equipment
- Various maps of Europe and Africa including charts, topographical and other special maps

Surreptitious entry devices:

- 14 sets of wiretapping equipment
- 6 ultraviolet desk lamps
- 6 flashlights with ultraviolet filters
- 12 high-powered magnifying glasses
- 50 sets of lock-picking equipment

Operational Groups' Weapons and Stores

Weapons:

- 300 Martin 9-mm sub-machine guns
- 2 Winchester 12-gauge riot shotguns with 200 rounds of ammunition
- 4 Bren guns with 5000 rounds
- 4 .22 calibre Colts with 4000 rounds
- 4 .32 caliber pistols with 800 rounds
- 4 Luger pistols with 800 rounds
- 500 fighting knives
- 200 spring coshes

Sabotage Stores:

- 30,000 packets of plastic explosive (PE)
- 1000 magnets
- 1000 fog signals (special railway track switch fuses)
- 1000 universal switch fuses

- 1500 assorted universal time-delay pencil fuses
- 150 limpets
- 200 clams
- 1000 magnesium incendiaries
- 1000 assorted pocket time-delay incendiaries
- 100 striker bands (for igniting slow fuses)
- 5000 boxes of safety matches
- 500 No. 6 nonelectric caps
- 500 No. 8 blasting caps
- 20,000 ft of fine .014 gauge steel wire
- Vaseline in tubes

Other Items:

- 12 fully inflatable rubber boats with a like number of scaling ladders, wall hooks, wharf hooks, and knuckle dusters
- 12 smatchets
- 100 units of knockout drops
- 1200 units of L tablets (lethal)
- 75 square yards of rubber substitute fabric
- 30 pairs of gym shoes
- 600 Benzedrine tablets

Communications:

- Equipment for two field radio stations and one temporary station, including 20 No. 35 portable radios and items for unit training

Training School:

- 20 sets of charts for identification of uniforms, airplanes, ships, and weapons of Allied and enemy nations
- 4 sets of models of all weapons
- 35-mm slide and film projectors with sound
- Signal Corps equipment to train 25 students
- 500 Type "A" parachutes for large personnel with 500 jump suits and associated clothing
- 50 map boards and sets of map-reading equipment
- 50 dummy grenades

IDENTIFICATION CARDS, INSIGNIA, FAREWELL LETTER AND CERTIFICATE

Special Forces Wings: Worn by OSS and SOE graduates of the British Special Forces training schools. The "SF" wings are sometimes referred to as "JEDBURGH Wings" because they were most frequently seen worn by OSS personnel that had trained in England for JEDBURGH missions; black field, white wings, roundel in red, letters "SF" are in light blue.

OSS Insignia (full size):

Burma Campaign Bar: Sterling silver campaign bar worn by members of OSS Detachment 101. (shown top center)

OSS Lapel Badge: Issue lapel badge; gold spearhead on black field with gold edging. (shown center right)

Shoulder Flash: Gold thread on a black field. (shown bottom center)

OSS Lapel Pin: Enameled Pin; gold on a red field. (shown center left)

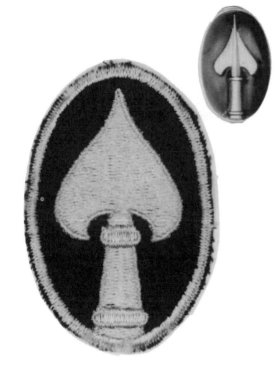

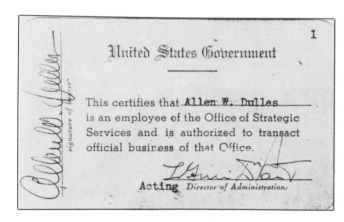

Identification Cards:

These identification cards were authorized and worn by OSS personnel in Washington, DC.

Type 1: Issued to Allen Dulles

Type 2: Worn by Ivar Bryce

Gen. Donovan's farewell letter to former members of the OSS. The letter accompanied the OSS veteran's lapel emblem that is shown in the upper left of the letter.

OFFICE OF STRATEGIC SERVICES
WASHINGTON 25, D. C.

28 September 1945

TO FORMER MEMBERS OF OSS:

It is my pleasure to forward to you the enclosed certificate commemorating your service in World War II as a member of the Office of Strategic Services. This certificate exemplifies in a tangible way my feeling that some such recognition should be given to the personnel of OSS as evidence of the resourcefulness, courage and devotion to duty shown by the men and women of the Agency who provided our Nation with an unprecedented service which hastened the day of victory.

To provide identification of the members of the organization, a group of former OSS associates has arranged for the design and manufacture of insignia available to those who are receiving certificates. The insignia is a lapel emblem which has the letters "OSS" stamped in gold on a red enamel background. At the request of this group there is enclosed herewith a coupon for the use of those who wish to procure such emblems.

I also enclose the text of remarks made at a meeting of OSS personnel held on 28 September, and a copy of President Truman's letter to me. The credit for OSS accomplishments belongs to the superior personnel who made them possible. I am deeply grateful for your loyal and effective contribution.

Sincerely,

William J. Donovan
Director

An original certificate of service given to veterans at the time of disbandment from the OSS. Each certificate was signed by Gen. Donovan, founder of the OSS.

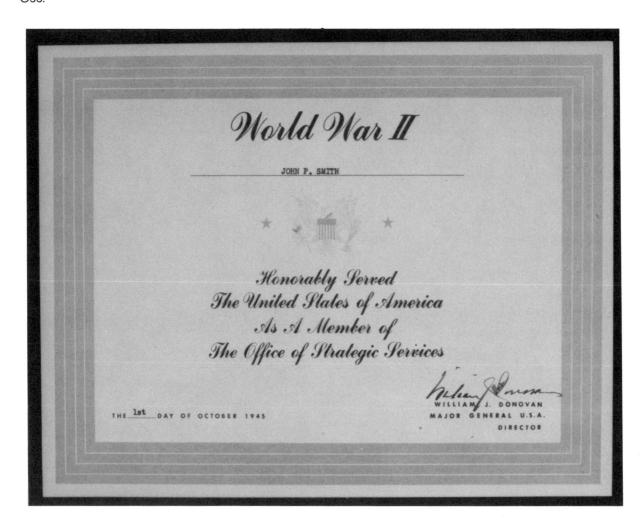

Glossary

OSS RESEARCH PROJECTS, SPECIAL DEVICES, AND TERMINOLOGY

Abalone: Methods of attaching limpet

Adams Plan: Use of bats carrying explosives (named for OSRD committee member and chairman of the Division B-9c "Special Problems" committee, Roger Adams)

Adhesive: Substance for attaching explosives above water to all manner of surfaces

AN/PRC-1: Portable, suitcase-size radio transmitter/receiver built by the US Army Signal Corps for the US Army Military Intelligence. The set was also used by the OSS.

AN/PRC-5: Small portable radio transmitter/receiver built by the US Army Signal Corps for the US Army Military Intelligence. The set was also used by the OSS.

Anerometer: A small, barometric switch intended to trigger an explosion in an airplane at approximately 1500 ft. higher than the elevation of the departure airfield

Aqua Vita: Producing sterile water from contaminated sources

Arson: Methods of instruction in use of fire

Aunt Jemima: Mix of RDX or HMX and flour that has properties of PE (high explosive), but can be camouflaged and transported as ordinary flour and even used in the preparation of biscuits and pancakes

Balsam: Edible, but humidity resistant, paper for easy destruction, on which writing can be made with both pen and pencil

Barney: Glass cloth cover for outboard motors

Beano: A baseball-size fragmentation grenade that explodes on impact

Belcher: Chemicals that make water undrinkable (but not poisonous) when introduced in extremely small quantities

Big Joe: The rifle-size version of the Penetrometer (see also)

Bigot: Adaptor for a .45 caliber automatic pistol to fire a finned projectile by the spigot mortar principle

Black Joe: Explosive coal

Blackout: High-explosive electric bulb that ignites when turned on

Brimstone: General problems with incendiary devices

Bull's-Eye: The use of scientific devices for the destruction of specific targets

Burp: British Urgent Railway Plan for derailing locomotives

Bushmaster: Three types of devices, using time delays, to produce simulated rifle and machine-gun fire

Button Compass: A miniature compass concealed within a military uniform button of standard appearance

Caccolube: A device that attacks a combustion engine through contaminants (contained in a small rubber sack—prophylactic) introduced into the oiling system

Camel: Camouflage

Canister Locater: Device for reception parties to find containers easily after a night parachute drop

Cannon: Assassin's pistol

Capsules H: Delay capsules to be placed in combustible liquid to start a fire at a predetermined future time

Casey Jones: Methods of attacks on railways

City Slicker: A water-activated device intended to ignite oil slicks

Clam: A small explosive charge designed to be attached to vehicles and exploded by an attached time-delay pencil

Cluck: A communications device to identify friends and distinguish them from enemies in the dark or during a raid

COHQ: Combined Operations Headquarters

Cricket: The development of compact (portable) radio transmitters/receivers

Division 19: The "miscellaneous weapons" section of the NDRC

Dog Drag: A device employing strong-smelling liquids that prevents an agent from being tracked by dogs

Emily Post: Projects involving poisons

Facsimile: Transmitting reproductions of pictures or photographs through the use of communications wire

Fantasia: Psychological methods of frightening an enemy

Firefly: A hand-held, easily concealed, explosive device to be dropped into the fuel tank of an enemy vehicle

Fountain: A shaped explosive charge that is planted between the track rails for the purpose of destroying the boiler of a railway locomotive

Frisk Knife: A small knife designed to be taped flat against the arm or leg, and remain undiscovered during a search or "frisk"

Gilhooley: A portable, briefcase-size kit for making photographic duplications

Glove Pistol: A .38 caliber firing device mounted on the back of a heavy leather work glove

Hedy: A nonlethal device intended to cause panic in large crowds

Honeymoon: Work on methods of making time-delay fuses

Hooter: An underwater noise device used by ships and submarines to home in on a small craft carrying raiding personnel or others returning to a rendezvous

IFT and IFL: Electromagnetic devices by which a man wearing an Induction Field Locator (IFL) can home in on an Induction Field Transmitter (IFT)

ISRB: Inter-Services Research Bureau; cover name for SOE (see also)

Joe Louis: A device for throwing grenades or small mortar shells through the use of the Penetrometer (see also)

Lacrima Tojo: Liquid explosive disguised as lubricating oil

Life Preserver: British terminology for the Spring Cosh (see also)

Limpet: Device used for underwater attacks on stationary ships

Little Joe: A small, hand-held version of the Penetrometer (see also)

Lockpick Knife: A portable lockpick kit camouflaged as a small penknife

Locust: The sabotage of precision machine equipment by small quantities of chemicals

Lost Chord: A communications and homing device for agents

Lulu: A dispersal and ignition device for inflammable dust

M-209: Small, portable, rotor-based cipher machine

Match Box: An ultraminiature 16-mm camera designed to be easily concealed and camouflaged as a box of matches

Matchhead: Waterproofed igniter made of celluloid or magnesium for the silent ignition of incendiaries

Maude Miller: Destroying tropical foliage

Minox: An ultraminiature 11-mm camera originally built in Riga, Latvia

MI-9: Division of British Intelligence specializing in Escape and Evasion

MIS-X: Secret US military organization that produced escape and evasion equipment for Allied POW's

Mole: A light-sensitive explosive switch designed to ignite an explosion when a train enters a tunnel

Moth: Special incendiary briefcases and notebooks that may be rapidly destroyed

MRL: Maryland Research Laboratories

MWT: A secure communications device utilizing microwave frequencies

NDRC: National Defense Research Committee

Nemo: Attacks on submarines

Odometer: Special fuse switch designed to ignite an explosive charge after a train has travelled a preset distance

One-Time Pad: A method of sending and receiving ciphered messages that uses a pad of unique numbers. The matching numbers on each pad are generated in a manner to approach randomness. The sender and the receiver possess the only copies of pads. After being used only "One Time," both sets of pads are destroyed

ONI: Office of Naval Intelligence

OSRD: Office of Scientific Research and Development

Paul Revere (PR): Incendiary capable of igniting crude oil

PE: Plastic explosive

Penetrometer: Silent and flashless weapon that fires a dart or other object using rubber as a catapult

Pin-Up: Device for attaching a limpet to the hull of a ship through the use of an explosive nail

Pneumonia: Methods of causing sudden death through means that go undetected

Pocket Incendiary: A portable device designed to start a delayed fire with an intense flame

Postell: Methods of using enemy-controlled telephone wires

Press-X: A portable, hand-operated, miniature offset printing press

Rainbow: Ultraviolet and infrared communications systems

Saint Michael: magnetic recorder, microphone, and telephone-line attachment

Salex: A slow-burning explosive of sulphur, aluminum powder, and TNT

SCR-504: Portable, direction-finding suitcase radio designed to locate clandestine radio transmissions. The set was designed and built by the US Army Signal Corps for Military Intelligence. The set was extensively used by the OSS

SFHQ: Special Forces Headquarters, London; Office in London that coordinated OSS and SOE activities

Shell: Use of cashew nut oil to sabotage motor vehicles

Shortstop: Sabotage of electrical equipment by means that are not obvious, and therefore difficult to detect

Simultaneous Events: A radio-controlled switch, safe from being accidentally triggered

Sky Wave: A special ground antennae for radio signals

Sleeping Beauty: Code-name for SOE designed one-man (canoe) submarine

Smatchet: Large, heavy, hand-held bladed weapon. The name is derived from the words "smashing" and "hatchet."

SOE: British Special Operations, Executive

Speedometer: A fuse activated by centrifugal force when fixed to the axle of railroad equipment

Spigot Mortar: A silent, flashless weapon developed by the British for attacks on enemy vehicles

Spring Cosh: A hand-held weapon that inflicts damage through the whipping action of a lead weight attached to the end of two concentric springs that telescope from a metal cylinder carried in the hand

SSTR-1: Special Services Transmitter/Receiver-Model No. 1. The first portable (suitcase-size) radio station designed by OSS Communications

SSTR-5: Special Services Transmitter/Receiver-Model No. 5. The final, and smallest, radio set produced in early 1945 by OSS Communications

Stinger: A small (cigarette-size) .22 caliber firing device designed for easy concealment

Sympathetic Fuse: A fuse that is triggered by an underwater explosion within close proximity

Thermit[e] Well: Designed to destroy metal machinery by cutting through the casing steel with a stream of 5000 degree Fahrenheit molten iron

Time Delay Pencil: A pencil-size object that lets an agent trigger an explosive (or other) device at a predictable future time

Tire Spike: A small metal spike designed to be thrown onto roadways and airfield runways in order to puncture rubber tires

Turtle Egg: See Caccolube

Type A, Mark II: Compact, three-module briefcase-size transmitter/receiver radio designed for the SOE. The radio was evaluated by the OSS and the subsequent SSTR-1 was based on this design and configuration. Some early OSS personnel trained on the Type A, Mark II while in England.

Type A, Mark III: The smallest of the powerful briefcase transmitter/receiver radio sets produced by the SOE in World War II. American Jedburgh radio operators were trained on this set.

Type B, Mark II: The most powerful and most successful of SOE radio sets (transmitter/receiver) produced during World War II. This suitcase radio was the "workhorse" set used and preferred by both American and British graduates of the SOE training schools.

UWT: Underwater device for communications between Sleeping Beauty submarines (see also)

Varga: A charge shaped to split open and set fire to oil storage tanks

Veritas: A delayed-action device for firing signal flares dropped from an aircraft

Vitamin Pills: Capsules of special chemicals that when dissolved in water are undetectable by normal testing, but are capable of destroying electric storage batteries

Welbike: A small portable motorbike designed to fit within a standard parachute container

Welfag: .22 caliber firing device concealed within a cigarette

Welpen: A firing device concealed within a fountain pen that was capable of firing either tear gas or a projectile

Welpipe: .22 caliber firing device concealed within a smoking pipe

Welrod: An automatic pistol with integral suppressor (silencer) designed at the secret SOE laboratory (Welwyn Experimental Laboratory) north of London

Who Me?: A device intended to harass the enemy by contaminating his clothing with a foul-smelling skatolic substance

William Tell: The final model of the Penetrometer

Wire: An alloy of aluminum, with adequate electrical and mechanical properties, yet which dissolves in salt water

Woodchuck: A device to wreck a train on a bridge

Woolworth Gun: An inexpensive stamped metal pistol designed to be produced in large quantities and dropped to resistance units

Zephyr: Silencing outboard motors

Bibliography

Applegate, Major Rex. *Kill or Get Killed: A Manual of Hand-To-Hand Fighting*. Harrisburg, Penn.: Military Service Publishing Co., 1943.

Bryce, Ivar. *You Only Live Twice: Memories of Ian Fleming*. Frederick, Md.: University Publications of America Inc., 1984.

Buerlein, Bob. *Allied Military Fighting Knifes*. Richmond, Va.: American Historical Foundation, 1984.

Fairbairn, Major W.E. *Get Tough*. New York: D. Appleton-Century Company, 1943.

Fieser, Louis F. *The Scientific Method: A Personal Account of Unusual Projects in War and Peace*. New York: Reinhold Publishing Corporation, 1964.

Fraser-Smith, Charles and Sandy Lesberg. *The Secret War of Charles Fraser-Smith*. London: Michael Joseph Ltd., 1981.

Hutton, Clayton. *Official Secret*. New York: Crown Publishers, 1961.

Kahn, David. *The Codebreakers: The Story of Secret Writing*. New York: The Macmillan Company, 1967.

Ladd, James and H. Keith Melton. *Clandestine Warfare: Weapons and Equipment of the SOE and OSS*. London: Blandford Press, 1988.

Lorain, Pierre. *Clandestine Operations: The Arms and Techniques of the Resistance, 1941–1945*. New York: Macmillan Publishing Company, 1983.

McLean, Donald B. *The Plumber's Kitchen: The Secret Story of American Spy Weapons*. Wickenberg, Ariz.: Normount Technical Publications, 1975.

Minnery, John and Joe Ramos. *American Tools of Intrigue*. Cornville, Ariz.: Desert Publications, 1980.

Minnery, John. *Firearm Silencers: Volume Two*. Cornville Ariz.: Desert Publications, 1981.

Normount Technical Publications. *O.S.S. Special Weapons, Devices and Equipment*. Wickenberg, Ariz.: 1975.

Roosevelt, Kermit. *War Report of the OSS*. U.S. Government, 1947. Declassified 17 July 1975.

Russell, Francis and the Editors of Time-Life Books. *The Secret War*. Alexandria, Va.: Time-Life, 1981.

Shoemaker, Lloyd R. *The Escape Factory*. New York: St. Martin's Press, 1990.

Skennerton, I.D. *De Lisle's Commando Carbine*. Australia: Small Arms Series, 1981.

Troy, Thomas F. *Donovan and the CIA: A History of the Establishment of the Central Intelligence Agency*. Frederick, Md.: University Publications of America, Inc., 1981.

Index

Accessories
  adhesive paste and tape, 100
  button compass, 113
  detonator magazine and magnets, 102
  escape kit, 112
  escape knife, 111
  Gilhooley, 107
  jump suit, 117
  lockpick knife, 110
  Match Box (camera), 103–104
  medical kit, 109
  Minox miniature camera, 105–106
  plastic explosive and Primacord, 101
  Press X, 108
  Sleeping Beauty, 114–115
  Welbike, 116
AC delay, 97–98
Adhesive paste, 100
Adhesive tape, 100
Air-Pen, 48
Anerometer, 67–68
AN/PRC-1 suitcase radio, 74
AN/PRC-5 suitcase radio, 75
Arteries, vulnerable to knife attack, 16
Automotive attack, 85–89
Beano, 69
Belt-Gun, 39
Bigot, 44
Button compass, 113
Caccolube, 86–87
Cameras
  Match Box, 103–104
  Minox miniature, 105–106
Canoe, motorized submersible (Sleeping Beauty), 114–115
Capsules H, 57
Certificates, 122
Cigarette, .22 caliber, 31
Cigar pistol, 33
Cipher device or machine
  M-94, 81
  M-209, 79–80
  One-Time Pad, 82
City Slicker, 55
Clam, 62–63
Close combat weapon, Peskett, 27
Coal camouflage kit, 71
Colby, William, 5–6
Colt pistol, .32 caliber, 40
Communications equipment
  cipher devices, 79–82
  SCR-504 direction-finding radio, 76
  SSR-5 miniature radio, 73
  suitcase radios, 72, 74–75, 77–78
Compass, button, 113
Contact-paper printer, Gilhooley, 107
Cosh, spring, 24–25
Crossbows
  hand-held, 45
  shoulder-fired, 46
Dart-Pen, 47
DeLisle carbine, 43
Detonator magazine, 102
Dog drag, 84
Donovan, General William, 10, 121
En-Pen, 30
Escape kit, 112
Escape knife, 111
Explosives
  anerometer, 67–68
  Beano, 69
  clam, 62–63
  coal camouflage kit, 71
  explosive coal, 70
  fog signal, 64

Limpet, 58–59
Mole, 65–66
Pin-Up Girl, 60–61
Fairbairn system, 15
Fighting knife, 15
Firefly (incendiary explosive), 85
Firing devices
  AC delay, 97–98
  MK.3 (clock), 99
  pressure type A-3, 90–91
  pull type A-2, 94
  release type A-2, 92–93
  time delay pencils, 95–96
Fog signal, 64
Frisk knife, 20
Garrote, 26
Gilhooley, 107
Glove pistol, 38
Gravity knife, 21
Guns. See also Pistol(s); specific guns
  sub-machine, silenced barrel for M3 .45 caliber, 41
Harassing agents, 83–84
Identification cards, 120
Incendiaries
  Capsules H, 57
  City Slicker, oil slick igniter, 55
  packet, 56
  pocket incendiary M1, 49–50
  Thermit Wells, 51–54
Insignia, 119, 120
Jump suit, 117
Knives
  arteries vulnerable to attack, 16
  escape, 111
  fighting, 15
  Frisk, 20
  gravity, 21
  lapel, 19
  lockpick, 110
  Saboteur's, 89
  sleeve dagger, 18
  small fighting, 16–17
  Smatchet, 22–23
Knuckles, 28
Lapel knife, 19
Large Thermit Well, 51–52
Letter of farewell, 121
Liberator (Woolworth gun), 34–35
Limpet, 58–59
  with pinning device, 60–61
Little Joe, 45
Lockpick knife, 110
Magnets, 102
Match Box (camera), 103–104
M-94 cipher device, 81
M-209 cipher machine, 79–80
Medical kit, 109
Miniature radio, SSR-5, 73
Minox miniature camera, 105–106
MK.3 (clock), 99
Mole, 65–66
National Defense Research Committee (NDRC)
  history of, 8
  organization of, 9
Office of Strategic Services Organization (OSS)
  globe emblem, 14
  organizational chart, 11
  Research and Development Branch, 11–12
  supplies at Algiers base, spring 1943, 118–119
Off-set printing press (Press X), 108
Oil slick igniter, 55

One-Time Pad, 82
OSS. See Office of Strategic Services Organization
Pencils, time delay, 95–96
Pen-shaped weapons, 30, 47–48
Personal weapons
  Air-Pen, 48
  cigarette, .22 caliber, 31
  cigar pistol, 33
  crossbows, 45–46
  Dart-Pen, 47
  En-Pen, 30
  garrote, 26
  knives, 15–23
  knuckles, 28
  Peskett close combat weapon, 27
  pistols, 32–44
  spring cosh, 24–25
  Stinger, 29
Peskett close combat weapon, 27
Pin-Up Girl, 60–61
Pistol(s)
  Belt-Gun, 39
  Bigot, 44
  cigar, 33
  Colt, .32 caliber, 40
  glove, 38
  Liberator (Woolworth gun), 34–35
  pipe, 32
  silenced .22 caliber automatic, 36–37
Plastic explosive (P.E.) and Primacord, 101
Pocket incendiary M1, 49–50
Pressure-type A-3 firing device, 90–91
Press X, 108
Pull-type A-2 firing device, 94
Radio, SCR-504 direction-finding, 76
Release-type A-2 firing device, 92–93
Rifle, Sniper's with silencer, 42
Saboteur's knife, 89
SCR-504 direction-finding radio, 76
Silenced barrel for M3 .45 caliber sub-machine gun, 41
Silenced .22 caliber automatic pistol, 36–37
Sleeping Beauty, 114–115
Sleeve dagger, 18
Small fighting knife, 16–17
Smatchet, 22–23
Sniper's rifle with silencer, 42
Special Forces Wings, 119
Spring cosh, 24–25
Stinger, 29
Sub-machine gun, silenced barrel for M3 .45 caliber, 41
Suitcase radios
  AN/PRC-1, 74
  AN/PRC-5, 75
  SSTR-1, 72
  Type A, Mark II, 78
  Type B, Mark II, 77
Terminology, 123–126
Thermit wells
  large, 51–52
  small, 53–54
Time delay pencils, 95–96
Tire spike, 88
Type A, Mark II suitcase radio, 78
Type B, Mark II suitcase radio, 77
Welbike, 116
Welrod, 37
Who, Me?, 83
William Tell, 46
Wire, garrote, 26
Woolworth gun, 34–35